POETRY COM

GREAT MINDS

Your World...Your Future...YOUR WORDS

From Stoke-on-Trent

Edited by Aimée Vanstone

 Young**Writers**

First published in Great Britain in 2005 by:
Young Writers
Remus House
Coltsfoot Drive
Peterborough
PE2 9JX
Telephone: 01733 890066
Website: www.youngwriters.co.uk

SB ISBN 1 84460 711 9

Foreword

This year, the Young Writers' 'Great Minds' competition proudly presents a showcase of the best poetic talent selected from over 40,000 up-and-coming writers nationwide.

Young Writers was established in 1991 to promote the reading and writing of poetry within schools and to the youth of today. Our books nurture and inspire confidence in the ability of young writers and provide a snapshot of poems written in schools and at home by budding poets of the future.

The thought, effort, imagination and hard work put into each poem impressed us all and the task of selecting poems was a difficult but nevertheless enjoyable experience.

We hope you are as pleased as we are with the final selection and that you and your family continue to be entertained with *Great Minds From Stoke-on-Trent* for many years to come.

Contents

Daniel Rowley (13)   25
David Marsh (13)   26
Michael Priestley (14)   26
Aimee Calcott (13)   27
Hayley Gidman (15)   27
Sally Malbon (13)   28
Melissa Smallwood (15)   28
Rachel Wakelin (13)   29
Dean Tymczuk (15)   29
Hannah Lowe (15)   30
Becky Clarkson (13)   30
Kieran Irving (14)   31
Kay Harrison (14)   31
James Kelly (14)   32
Natalie Cooper (14)   32
Michelle Poole (15)   33
Jordan Diskin (14)   33
Chantel Kaur (15)   34
Charlotte Woodward (15)   34
Kelly Brindley (14)   35
Emma Harris (14)   35
Sarah Brennan (14)   36

Maryhill High School

Zara Owen (11)   36
Jacob Woolhouse (11)   36
Jordan Rigby (12)   37
Alex Gould (11)   37
Francesca Lascelles (11)   37
Harriet Mullington (12)   38
Kieran Walker (11)   38
Heather Porter (12)   39
Lisa Stephenson (11)   40
Samantha Jordan (11)   40
Joshua Ellis (11)   41
Jessica Gallimore (11)   41
Nicola Belfield (11)   42
Bethany Bowker (11)   42
Sam Harris (12)   43
Megan Booth (11)   43
Darrien Lowe (12)   44

Rebecca Unyolo (12)	74
Thomas Wilcox (13)	75
Danielle Roberts (13)	76
Isaac Cooke (11)	76
Ben Gascoigne (15)	77
Ben Cartwright (11)	77
Laura Warrilow (11)	78
Siân Metcalf (11)	78
Thomas Brough (11)	79
Thomas Harriden (11)	79
Amy Plant (11)	80
Matthew Fone (11)	80
Nicola Regan (13)	81
Lindsey Alcock (13)	82
Callum O'Rourke (11)	83
Matthew Hurst (15)	84
Elizabeth Lloyd (11)	84
Emma Jackson (13)	85
Eleanna Parkinson (11)	85
Alisha White (11)	86
Matt Capper (15)	86
Alice Jarvis (15)	87
Gareth Mycock (13)	88
Ashley Griffiths (12)	88
Samantha Booth (15)	89
Jake Clarke (12)	90
Katie Seaton	90
Thu Anh Nguyen (11)	91
Christopher Bevans (15)	91
Ross Daniels (15)	92
Ben Willis (13)	93
Christopher Toplass (11)	93
Declan Worrall (11)	94
Daniel Harrison (11)	94
Jodie Carnwell (11)	95
Thomas Roughton (13)	95
Josh Leech (11)	96
Jack Ward (11)	96
James Homer (12)	97
Sophie Wye (14)	97
Rachael Jackson (11)	98
Sophie Mills (11)	98

Gemma Bailey (11)	99
James Bailey (11)	99
Joseph Rapacchietta (11)	100
Siobhan Killeen (11)	100
Chelsey Baggley (11)	101
Samuel Freeman	101
Helen Wood (13)	102
Beverley Rushton (11)	102
Carly Plant (13)	103
Lexie Hankinson (13)	103
Will Tatlow (13)	104
Liam O'Neill (13)	104
Josh McVeigh (13)	105
Elliott Bateman (13)	105
Elizabeth Harper (13)	106
Lorna Horton (14)	107
Kirsty Shaw (11)	108
Jessica Roberts (12)	108
Jake Ufton (12)	109
Adam McLeod (13)	109
Thomas Bland (12)	110
Christopher Ward (14)	110
Jonathan Wooldridge (12)	111
Nathan Alcock (13)	111
Amy Plant (12)	112
Catherine Deaville (11)	112
Alex Bamford (12)	113
Nicky Roberts (12)	113
Matthew Forrester (12)	114
Joe Marlow (14)	115
Katy Buttress (13)	116
Jamie Capper (12)	116
Alexander Humphreys (15)	117
Philippa Whitmarsh (13)	117
Hannah Richardson (15)	118
David Hancock (13)	119
Cian Carroll (14)	120
Tyler Starkey (13)	121
Lorna Poole (16)	122
Philip Milward (16)	123
Leona Mould (13)	124
Trevor Oliver (11)	124

Ashley Rommelrath (14)	125
Charlotte Bee (12)	125
Jonathan Salt (14)	126
Kieren Yates (11)	126
James Beattie (14)	127
Sally Mountford (12)	127
Adam Newport (12)	128
Abbi-Gayle Lindop (12)	128
Nikki Lamonby (12)	129
Tom Goodwin (11)	129
Laura Pemberton (12)	130
Lisa Cotton (15)	130
Christopher Allsop (11)	131
Sarah Rushton (15)	131
Siobhan Wallace (12)	132
Natalie Wolff	132
Christopher Millward (15)	133
Rosalyn Greatbatch (15)	133
Elisa Etemad (15)	134
James Morgan (12)	135
Jennifer Keeling (15)	135
Andrew Cope (15)	136
David Fisher (11)	137
Jenette Graham (15)	137
Joanne Healey (15)	138
Michael Tyers (13)	138
Ryan Hurst (12)	139
David Goodwin (13)	139
Tom Sims (12)	140
Liam Mountford (11)	140
Joseph Swanston (11)	141
William Campbell (12)	141
James Wood (15)	142
Olivia Healy (11)	143
Samantha Bloor (11)	144
Alex Oakden (13)	144
Lisa Dawson (11)	145
Siobhan Williams (11)	145
Jacob Collier (11)	146
Oliver McLeod (11)	146
Kirsty Brassington (11)	147
Emma Gotham (11)	147

Cathryn Button (12)	167
Steven Wareham (12)	167
Ben Mothershaw (13)	168
Luke Adams (13)	168
Alex Jones (12)	169
Daniel Ward (13)	169
Rachel Sedgwick (12)	170
Patrick Walters (12)	170
Rebecca Ward (12)	171
Alexandra Foulkes (12)	172
Katrina Earley (12)	173
Becky Hickey (12)	173
Luke Finney (11)	174

St Joseph's College

Philippa Pointon (14)	174
Stephanie Lakin (13)	175
Francesca Jones (13)	175
Róisín Bartlam (13)	176
Matthew Bailey (13)	176
Daniel Taylor (14)	176
Rajvir Sangha (13)	177
Imran Pirmohamed (13)	177

St Thomas More Catholic College

James Thorley (11)	178
Calum Edwards (12)	178
Katie Louise Jones (13)	179
Gemma Cammillare (13)	179
Roxanne Wilton (11)	180
Laura Rickard (12)	181
Chloe Ball (13)	182
Richard Tranah (12)	182
Matthew Keeling (13)	183
Lisa Darlington (13)	183
James Clarke (11)	184
Adam Foster (13)	184
Lee Finch (13)	185
Lewis Kenny (11)	185
Liam Dobson (13)	186
Kenneth Iredia (13)	186

Thomas Edwards (13)	187
Teresa Brammer (12)	187
Jade Bentley (14)	188
Amanda Preece (13)	188
Emma Jordan (13)	189
Jamie Coleman (13)	190
Daniel Gooding (11)	190
Amy Ostrouchow (14)	191
Kate Harrington (12)	191
Zoe Wheat (13)	192
Kelsey Franklin (12)	192
Laura Hulme (13)	193
Luke Melhado (11)	193
Tom Keeling (14)	194
Mitchell Barnett (11)	194
Matthew O'Rourke (13)	195
Conal O'Reilly (11)	195
Jake Harris (11)	196
Charlotte Stubbs (13)	196
Rachel Titchener (17)	196
Amanda Kerr (17)	197
William Hilditch (13)	197
Hannah Powell (16)	198
Elsa-Marie Evans (13)	198
Sally Horton (15)	199
Rebecca May Dudley (13)	199
Joseph Allen (15)	200
Abbey Hopkinson (11)	200
Patrick Hearne (14)	201
Jodee Colclough (17)	201
Madeline Martin (14)	202
Elisa Hearne (15)	202
Alex Brough (15)	203
Kim Sherwin (14)	204
Damian Rowe (15)	205
Michelle Owen (14)	206
Rachel Becker (15)	206
Natalie Davies (15)	206
Gemma Dawson (15)	207
Rachel Mannion (14)	208
Charlotte Preece (14)	208
Sadia Khalil (14)	209

Tom Daniel (12)   230
Lois Stevenson (11)   230
Michael Plant (12)   231
Joel Niemczyk (11)   231
Jake Rushton (12)   232
Rebecca Howells (11)   232
Geoffrey Knott (12)   233
Danielle Jenkinson (11)   233
Thomas Lavelle (12)   234
Jack Gratton (11)   234
Amy Cross (12)   235
Kieran Smith (11)   235
Sophie Cork (12)   236
Lucy Whitfield (12)   236
Sarah Griffiths (13)   237
Rhiannon Colclough (11)   237
Liam Brannigan (12)   238
Rachel Dimmock (11)   238

Sir Thomas Boughey High School
Carmen Gater (13)   239
Stephen Birch (14)   239
Nicola Platt (13)   240
Jake Peever (14)   240
Samantha Brooks (13)   241

The Poems

Dad (Anger)

Starting at a new school,
Little bit nervous,
Had a good day though.
That wasn't to last.
You left us in the living room
Watching TV.
You went upstairs and pondered
What you were going to say.
Mum came home at six
And you gave us our tea,
Then you took her upstairs
To tell her your story.
You came down,
All spruced up
In your shirt and tie.
I looked at you
And you looked at me;
I knew something was wrong,
I knew what was to come,
It didn't stop it hurting though
What you'd done to Mum.
You were leaving us.
Mum, brother and me.
I stared and stared,
How could you, how could you?
And then you were gone,
Out the door
And driving down the hill.
I couldn't believe my dad
Had left us standing there.

Samantha Higgins (15)
Biddulph High School

Anger

I wanted to go on,
I wanted to continue,
But soon I'd have to work.
It was that, that made me feel blue.

The minutes all flew by,
I was running out of time.
I had to stop this soon,
I was going to lose my mind.

But something wouldn't let me,
It wouldn't let me stop.
I was so close to giving up now,
I'd almost finished the lot.

But still and still they called me,
I had to tear away,
I paused for just a second,
And slowly walked away.

And so I did the work,
It wasn't really a lot,
And when I came back to my room
I could pick up where I left off.

And when I finished the game,
I felt so satisfied.
It overcame the anger,
The anger deep inside.

Michael Bond (16)
Biddulph High School

If I Sit . . .

If I sit, watch and listen,
I see and hear the conversations
Of friends about their lives.

The lives they live out of my company,
And though they are entitled
To their privacy, I can't help it hurting.

I cannot control or say how they
Should or shouldn't live, no matter
If they are happy with it or not.

I cannot interfere with matters that do not matter
To the matters of my life.
But I still want to be involved.

I still want to be wanted.
I still long to be loved.

James Hart (17)
Biddulph High School

Anger

I'm so nice to her,
I'm friends with her
And she throws it in my face.
I apologise and say I'm sorry,
I can't help being ill.
That one day that I let her down
And said that I couldn't go,
She was mean to me
And ignored me.
I don't understand why she feels it was wrong!

Now I feel lonely,
Guilty inside,
Even though I know I couldn't help it,
I feel that I've let her down.

Alice Russell (15)
Biddulph High School

Anger And Hatred

The fires burned within me
And my eyes both turned to flame.
He smiled like an idiot,
I'll forever curse his name.

'Will you go out with me?' he asked,
Putting his arm around my waist.
'I really fancy you,' he said,
I wanted to spit in his face.

I tried to escape his grip
As I had done so often before,
But there's no room to struggle,
Trapped in a corridor.

His face came up closer to mine,
I wished he was in Hell.
I thought I'd die from anger,
But then! Saved by the bell.

I thought it would go on forever,
He'd haunt me throughout my life,
He just wouldn't stop bugging me,
Unless I became his wife.

I hated the very sight of him,
The Devil incarnate.
If he had kept on doing it,
He would have deserved his fate.

Hannah Whitehurst (15)
Biddulph High School

Would You?

If I ran away from you,
Would you chase me?

If I hid from the world,
Would you reveal me?

If I stood up to leave you,
Would you beg me to stay?

If I found everything hard,
Would you help me?

If I cried on your shoulder,
Would you comfort me?

If I smiled and laughed,
Would you join me?

If I hurt you,
Would you forgive me?

If I told you I loved you,
Would you leave me alone?

Would you be there when I needed you?
Would you be there when I didn't?

Would you?

Nicola Brennan (15)
Biddulph High School

A Dream

Every night I sit and dream,
I dream of a land just over the horizon.
A land full of love and laughter,
A land that is free and equal.
Not like this land, full of war and grief.
Not like this land, full of death and hatred.
I dream of lush green countryside
And cheerful, gurgling streams.
I dream of the birds that flit through the trees,
Of the bees that hum busily in their hives.
Not like the dull, colourless place that I live in,
Not of the colour-drained gardens that were once so vibrant.
Maybe I dream of a time when life was colourful and full of laughter.
Maybe I dream of the times before hatred and evil were discovered.
I think I dream of this land as it used to be,
Yet it feels like a distant place.
Just out of sight . . .
Maybe life will be colourful again.
Maybe . . . just maybe.
But for now, I sit and dream of that land, just over the horizon.

Polly Russell (13)
Biddulph High School

Blood, Sweat And Tears

Blood is for emotion,
Hatred, anger, love,
Sweat is for the effort,
Hardship from above,
Tears are for the turmoil,
The fountain made inside,
Sadness comes from loving,
While we're on this ride,
The tears are falling softly,
Mingling with this sweat of mine,
Blood is on my dagger,
It gives the blade a shine,
They mix together swiftly,
Blood with sweat and tears,
All the pain and sorrow,
I've gathered through the years,
Laid resting in this puddle,
Which shines so sweet and pure,
And as my life is draining,
My dagger hits the floor.

Sarah Kirkham (13)
Biddulph High School

My Arms

Look at my arms,
The white shadow lines drawn across them,
Them . . . they made me do it,
Those words they chose,
So effectively,
To worm their way inside of me,
They strangled my heart and made me lose my mind,
That pain needed to be set free,
That pain of mine,
Inside of me,
Must be set free,
The blade smiled at me malevolently,
It cut through me like butter,
The red wine rose in the deep dips,
The pains inside of me have been set free,
The knife digs deeper into me to mine the last pain-ore,
With each dig deeper that red wine rises,
I feel like screaming,
I cry bitter tears of resentment,
A new pain has come,
But my bittersweet tears drown it out,
What I did made me feel so much better,
But the pain came home.
I set it free,
But each time it echoed back,
Louder and louder,
Worse and worse,
Look at my arms,
The white shadow lines draw across,
Them . . . they made me do it.

Hannah Miller (15)
Biddulph High School

The Breville Monkey

There's a monkey in the corner,
A monkey with a name,
A monkey that was used for science,
That is how he came
To be my little monkey,
The little one I own,
To everyone for miles around,
He's Breville Monkey known!

He sit in his own corner,
Responding to a clap,
Making a cheese sandwich,
Monkey's good at that,
Any kind of filling
My monkey friend can bring,
Sitting in his corner,
He can even sing!

He dances in his corner
To the music in his head,
Only taking off his hat
When he goes to bed,
Monkey's got a trike
That takes him everywhere,
Riding round all day long,
Doesn't have a care.

Tom Kirkham (13)
Biddulph High School

Isolation

As you sit there, it's so cold and boring,
You hear something, it sounds like snoring.
Your neighbour, beside you, fast asleep,
You sigh and have a hasty peep.
Wishing you could that easily rest your head,
You start to think about your bed.
Your covers, though they may not be clean,
Are still a more restful place to lean
Than the solid desks, so cold and dry,
The floor looks like a nicer place to lie.
Whilst sitting there, your thoughts they roam,
Just wishing it was time for you to go home.

David Pearson (14)
Biddulph High School

Emotions

There are so many feelings people feel,
But my life goes around like a Ferris wheel,
Forever turning me upside down,
Over, under, about and around.

Confused, don't know how to control my feelings,
I had a life without a meaning.
People say I was being stupid,
But I guessed I would never be struck by Cupid.

Questions, questions, they have no end,
I felt as if I had no friends.
All alone and confused,
My heart is broken and also bruised.

Just look at me now, lying underground,
Just lying there, making no sound.

Stephanie Adams (13)
Birches Head High School

What Should I Do?

What should I do?

My grandad wants me to
Be a doctor.

What should I do?

My dad wants me to
Be a lawyer.

What should I do?

My brother wants me to be
Famous and sing.

What should I do?

My uncle wants me to be
A footballer and play on a women's side.

What should I do?

My auntie wants me to
Ride horses all day, every day.

What should I do?

My nanna wants my life
To be great and successful.

What should I do?

My mum said she will back
My decision all the way,
So that is why I am a fashion designer
And life is great.

Jenna Barcroft (13)
Birches Head High School

The Beginning Of The Future

I'm lying on my bed,
What's going on inside my head?
What's happening to me?
Why can no one see?
It's just the same old me.

Why do I sometimes lose control?
It's like I'm playing a different role,
Sometimes I'm happy, sometimes I'm complicated,
Sometimes I'm miserable and sometimes I'm elated.
I'm as soft as a puppy but as devious as a shark,
But all I do is bark and bark.

So far my life has been laid out in front of my feet,
And I have only got one chance at life as I haven't got a receipt,
Some day I will be all alone and I'll spread my wings and fly,
Because in the real world there is no time to cry.
I've got to learn how to do things right and not to lose my temper,
And I'll have to know when to hold my tongue,
Count to five, not whimper,
But one day I will become the person that I want to be,
So now all that everyone else can do is watch, wait and see.

Bethany Di-Silvestro (13)
Birches Head High School

My Little Sister

My tears could have filled a pool,
My heart was filled with anguish,

When you left us, passed away,
All we had left was a wish.

If only you were still with us now,
We never did get over you.

That's why I'm standing here at your grave,
Saying, 'Little sister, I love you.'

Lydia Michalski (13)
Birches Head High School

A Girl In Love

He has played with her heart,
But still she won't let them part.
He says now he loves her,
She believes him, no matter what may occur.

When things go wrong,
She cries at night,
Lying there hugging her soft pillow tight,
Wishing and longing for him to come back.

He finds another love,
She is distraught with pain inside.
To him she explains how she feels,
But he still refuses to understand.

She asks herself,
Does he care?
What did he feel for her?
Did he love her?

Two weeks later he is back,
Her dreams have come true and there is nothing they lack.
He says he loves her,
No matter what may occur!

It's true,
She knows
This feeling,
It's love!

Sarah Roberts (13)
Birches Head High School

I Love You

You say you love me, I say I love you too,
I love you all over and I love you through,
Because this love we've got can never end,
How I ain't no joke or no five-minute friend.
Us for eternity, through to the end,
You love me girl, so don't pretend
That you hate me and we are only friends.
You see I have got a question to ask,
Will you extend this relationship
Right through to the end of our life?
Right through to the end of our great, happy life?
So marry me now and be my wife,
My wife for eternity.
If you've got any problems, you can turn to me,
I'll teach you things so you can learn from me.
You say no to all that I say to you,
If you're being like that I don't know what to do.
I have seen another girl, but I still want you,
So answer me this and answer me true,
Do you love me? Because I love you,
We're made for each other, we stick like glue.
If you stick with me, I will stick with you.
What, you say no, that me and you are through?
Don't try me anymore, go try something new,
Because me and you girl, damn, we're through.

Daniel Kolahi (13)
Birches Head High School

Winter Days!

The days are short,
The nights are long,
I think we've lost
The summer song.

With chilly winds
That blow so cold,
Where are the flowers,
Bright and bold?

Where robins hop
From tree to tree,
Gone is the busy
Bumblebee.

The moon hangs low
In a wintry sky,
I sit by the fire
But can't think why?

The seasons change
So quickly now.
I wonder why?
I wonder how?

Jemma Elsby (13)
Birches Head High School

Spooks

Whatever the fright,
All through the night
The witches come out,
The children shout
'Trick or treat'
Upon the street.

The pumpkin alights,
Something bites,
A spider runs past my feet,
I nearly fall off my seat.
It starts to get dark,
So we walk through the forest of bark.

We make our way
To the haunted house where we stay.
I go through the devilish door,
Where something sat staring,
It was big, it was scary,
And very, very hairy.
It lay on my bed,
Where it spookily said,
'Sleep tight.'

Michaela Mountford (12)
Birches Head High School

This Boy Of Mine

This boy of mine,
Forever and always
He makes me shine
In a lot more ways.

This boy of mine,
Don't let it be a phase,
You've taken me places
And sent me in a daze.

This boy of mine,
Just come with me,
Just take my hand
And you will see.

What you see is what you get,
I love you loads,
You won't regret.

Laura Sherwin (14)
Birches Head High School

A Tree - Haiku

Tree stands all alone
Swishing, swaying, all alone
Blatantly ignored.

Elliot Crouchley (13)
Birches Head High School

School Life

School life is a real bore,
Especially ours, which is poor.

The teachers are really mean,
The janitors are very unclean.

The headteacher does nothing but nap,
The school dinners are really crap.

All the students always fight,
The girls are a really horrible sight.

Lessons, rubbish, especially French,
In football you're on the bench.

The boys all think they are mega-great,
But they really look a terrible state.

The homework isn't easy,
Makes students quite queasy.

All in all, school ain't very nice,
Especially those infested by mice.

Zushan Hussain (13)
Birches Head High School

Friends Forever?

My friend is a friend
Who is always there,
She may be far,
But will always care.

I know for sure
That our friendship is true,
She supported me
In the painful times we went through.

We had moments
That were good and bad,
We stuck together
Through moments that were happy and sad.

Forever friends?
Well, we'll see,
Friends till the end
Is what we will be.

Aisha Ashraf (13)
Birches Head High School

Grandpa

Oh my loving grandpa,
I really miss you so.
I wish you never went away,
Why did you have to go?

Oh how I wish I had you here,
Hand in hand we'd be,
So as I shed my final tear,
I just want you to hear.

Three of your favourite words,
Joined to make one phrase,
These words I'm saying are so true,
No, it's not a phase.

The words, 'I love you',
They're what I want to say.
Grandpa how I love you,
And I'm sure you loved me too.

Amy Weaver (13)
Birches Head High School

I Dream

I dream about a meadow
Filled with daffodils
I dream about a river,
And waterfalls as steep as hills.
I dream about my school
And how well I want to do,
Also my nephew,
I dream about him too.
I dream about my dad,
How he always calls me Babe.
I dream about Eminem,
How he's never afraid.
I dream about my friends
And how they make me feel,
But most of all I dream about
How I wish these dreams were real.

Samantha Mee (12)
Birches Head High School

The Pre-Winter Weather

The autumn leaves are falling
And the weather is appalling,
That terrible wind is roaring,
Preventing birds from soaring.
These clouds don't have a silver lining,
They're stopping the sun from shining.
All the flowers are dying,
The weatherman's always lying.
But it makes no difference what we try to do,
The weather affects us all, including you.

Oliver Gotham (14)
Blurton High School

My Poem

Liverpool's champion's league dream starts here,
The crows assembled with cheer,
The anthems play
On this fine day,
Supporters filled with fear.
The whistle starts the game,
The team full of fame,
Kieran's fingers are crossed,
He thinks they've lost.
Each player thinks the same.
The final minutes run,
The pitch sparkles with fun.
It's still nil-nil,
But score if they will
Before the end has come.
The ball is up Liverpool's end,
So the opposition kicks a bend,
The opposition heads it in,
The Liverpool fans go dim
And the opposition celebrate their win!
Kieran stomped in his house, all grumpy and sore,
He stamped his feet and slammed the door.
He shouted and groaned and threw down his coat,
And made growling noises down his throat.
Then his mum said nervously, 'Don't worry, dear . . .
Liverpool might win a game next year!'

Daniel Boote (14)
Blurton High School

The Figure

I plod on slowly
To recognise
A man in black,
A solid disguise.
I turn and run,
Don't look back,
My journey begins
On a solid track.
He appears in front
And to the side,
I turn slowly,
He appears behind.
There's no space,
I begin to run
A rocky race,
Looks like I've won.
The pitch-black,
My only cloak.
Looks like I'm back.
I've just awoke.

Matthew Roberts (13)
Blurton High School

Dreaming - Tanka

I have been dreaming
Of hopes and second chances;
Where I may go back
And correct where I've been wrong.
Sadly, it's only a dream.

Carmen Dang (13)
Blurton High School

The World

The world should be full of peace and love,
This is what people are wishing from the heavens above.
All around there is shouting and fights,
Violence falls into the dark nights.
If only people would give in,
Put the world to rights and forget religion.
Why should different cultures change anything?
All the nasty words and name calling,
If all of this was to go away,
How would we be living in this world today?
Ambition and hope in everyone's minds,
Not shutting people out, we should all be kind.
So why not get on and make things better,
As we're all here in this world together?
If tomorrow was our last day on Earth,
Would we ever know what our lives were worth?

Kelly Causley (13)
Blurton High School

Early Winter Morning

The wind slithers by like a snake,
Thin layer of ice across the land,
The snow crunching . . . every step I take,
The pale numbness of my hand.

There's not a sound and not a word,
The snow is light, crisp and white.
No sound, no laughing, no noise to be heard.
It's pale, pure, clean and bright.

The crisp falling flakes drift and blow,
The sky is covered in a thin mist of grey.
They sparkle ice-white, lift and fly,
It becomes pitch-black, destroying the day.

Nicholas Johnson (13)
Blurton High School

School

S o many children pass through the gates year after year,
   bearing the memories of their school life.
C hildren laugh and cry in school.
H onest and good working children do well in school.
O utside, when they finish school, they go to college or get jobs.
O ver many years, teachers see thousands of faces, some more
   pleasant than others.
L ike school, if you don't, you'll find it very hard.

James Ibbs (13)
Blurton High School

Animals

A very hungry cub waiting for his mother
N obody loves him anymore.
I nside his heart, he had no sister nor a brother,
M aking his life a misery.
A lso, a badly injured horse lay in an open field,
L istening to the birds tweeting,
S unshine looking while he's sleeping.

Daniel Parsons (13)
Blurton High School

Battle For Salvation

Man's inner damnation will cause more battles
For it's within his mighty destiny.
Man shall always fight and the Earth shall rattle.
Can you resist the unforged destiny?
But man's urge to explore shall banish inner killings
And man shall share in greater earnings in life.

Daniel Rowley (13)
Blurton High School

Poetry

I stare at my blank piece of paper
When writing poetry,
I search my mind for inspiration,
Desperate not to waste another tree.
I have thought long and hard for hours,
Yet the rules of poetry torment me,
With tankas, rondeau and similes,
I just cannot find the right imagery.
Suddenly the light shines through,
I start using rhythm and rhyme,
The verse on the paper starts growing
And I am really having a good time,
So if you'd rather not write a poem,
But watch TV or go out to play,
You should think again, it can be fun
And the satisfaction it brings can make your day -
Hooray!

David Marsh (13)
Blurton High School

The Raging Storm

A torrential, gloomy night, they prepare
Their glorious galleon to set sail.
Although the crew are courageous to dare,
They risk their lives in the thunder and hail.
They ventured through the malevolent storm,
Their great galleon was sailing with ease,
But then a horrendous whirlpool did form
And a cyclone was conjured by the breeze.
The captain tightly grabbed hold of the wheel
And swiftly piloted their ship away,
The galleon fled as fast as an eel,
They all could live to see another day.
The storm died down and they could now see sand,
They were all relieved to set foot on land.

Michael Priestley (14)
Blurton High School

Water

Down the long rivers it flows,
Beneath the sun's rays it glows,
Down waterfalls it slashes,
As people play, it splashes.
When it rains it falls to the ground,
Then it's drunk by a cat or a hound.
It does not have a certain taste,
But yet it never goes to waste.
It can be found in many strange places,
That's why it attracts so many different paces.
It can be seen off piers and bays
As it travels its separate ways.
But just think about the people who have none,
And yet we think that it doesn't affect anyone.
But if you don't drink it, then you'll get shorter,
That's why you should drink plenty of water.

Aimee Calcott (13)
Blurton High School

My Mum

She is always worrying about tiny, little things,
Like money, bills and everything.
She didn't have a job, but I didn't care,
But still she bought me lovely clothes
That I loved to wear.
She always treats me like a spoilt child,
So I always have the latest style.
She always talks to me when I am feeling down,
And I know wherever I am, she will always be around.
I love going shopping with her, being with her and whatever,
And I hope we will still be together forever.
She is like an angel to me, as light as a feather,
And I will always love her, forever and ever.

Hayley Gidman (15)
Blurton High School

My Friend

Her name is Jade, she's as tall as a tree,
Her family treats me like one of them.
She's always been there looking out for me,
She used to go out with a boy named Ben.
My mum quite likes her, I hope hers likes me,
When she's in a bad mood, she can be dodgy,
But then she settles down and lets things be.
Her mum makes mashed potato which is stodgy
Oh! And as for her brother, he is noisy.
Whereas her sister, she is very quiet.
Her favourite actor is called Boisey.
Her sister is always trying to diet.
Her dog is small and very good-looking.
We all go out for family grouping.

Sally Malbon (13)
Blurton High School

Sports

Football and hockey are my favourite sports,
Table tennis, netball and many more.
Playing these regularly I am taught
The more you pass, the more chance you will score.
I love to play left inner in hockey,
In football I take corners and throw-ins.
I play in all weather, even when foggy,
When the whistle is blown we soon begin.
The sport coaches start to scream and shout
As the football studs make some small holes.
All the players that are rushing about,
Passing the ball and shooting in the goals.
All the different sports I have done,
I just remember to have lots of fun!

Melissa Smallwood (15)
Blurton High School

Emptiness

Now that you have gone,
It always seems to rain.
I sit there all alone
Feeling full of pain.

The room in which I sit
Is always full of stillness,
I think of you in that pit,
Lying dead and motionless.

I look across to see you
Sitting in your chair.
I went to say, 'I love you,'
Then realised you weren't there.

Now that my mind knows
I have got to move on,
I have to stop feeling low
And realise you are gone.

This is my last sentence,
I just want you to know,
I am feeling so intense
And I'm sorry to let you go.

Rachel Wakelin (13)
Blurton High School

Dinosaur

D angerous predator
I ncredible size
N asty animal
O utstanding surprise
S cary creature
A wesome teeth
U nusual appetite
R epulsive feet.

Dean Tymczuk (15)
Blurton High School

Mother Earth

She is walking all alone once again,
Staring at the moon with hatred in mind.
Why do they ignore her, she is in pain?
She did try her best to be good and be kind.
Why won't they listen, and what will she do?
She walks in bare feet in the cold, damp grass,
Sits on the littered concrete that's damp too.
All of this is driving her to madness.
She's watching the stars so calm and peaceful,
Why do they abuse her so, is it fair?
She's watching her own life flash by, awful,
What did she do wrong? They don't even care.
She will get her revenge, she will one day,
She is Mother Earth, and she will decay.

Hannah Lowe (15)
Blurton High School

No More

The river flows but nothing's in it,
The mind is open but nothing's on it,
The Earth does turn but nothing's round it,
The sun is bright but nothing sees it,
The air is crisp but nothing breathes it,
The animal desperately hunts but nothing's hunted,
The ice was freezing but now is rigid,
The life was living but now is dead,
The water is deadly so nothing soaks it,
The rock is ash so nothing climbs it,
The warmth is nothing, so cold is commanding,
The nights are dark but nothing sleeps,
The grass is lush but nothing can grow it,
The death is dire and so it will creep.

Becky Clarkson (13)
Blurton High School

Seasons

When springtime comes, lambs are born,
And the time has come to sow the corn.
Daffodils and tulips grow,
When warm the rivers begin to flow.

When the summer comes and the flower blooms,
All the kids leave their rooms,
And the sun shines
On everyone that he finds.

When the autumn comes and the leaves do fall,
I am lost within the beauty of it all.
Oranges, reds, yellows and greens,
May it all just be pleasant dreams?

When winter comes and the snow falls,
And children's boots are once again found in the halls,
Jack Frost takes hold of your toes,
And red does the chill turn your nose.

Kieran Irving (14)
Blurton High School

Love

Love is a lightning bolt shot from the sky,
Love is a cloud floating up high,
Love is so safe and secure,
But it never comes knocking at your door.

You are my cute, cuddly bear,
And we definitely make a perfect pair.
You are my saviour, you are my soul,
Because of you I now feel whole.

Kay Harrison (14)
Blurton High School

The Abyss

In the shallows where the swallows sleep,
Shifting uncomfortably in their slumber
However undisturbed in their eternal keep
Gliding so silently through the lumber.
While something stirs silently in the midst,
Swimming elegantly through the weeds,
Some fish bombard it to test its wits,
But soon find out not to mess with its needs.
Slaughtering poor creatures is what it does,
Grinding the fishes' brittle bones.
There's no stranger creature that no one loves
Crashing and destroying other fishes' homes.
Now it's awake, its ferocity is unmatched,
You are nothing, you must be dispatched.

James Kelly (14)
Blurton High School

Autumn

Children playing conkers all together,
Glancing up at the black, darkening sky,
Wrapping up warm against the cold weather,
Schoolchildren quickly hurrying by.
The freezing, silent nights are drawing in,
No green trees or brightly-coloured flowers,
Waiting for boring autumn to begin,
Only gusty winds and autumn showers.
There's not a happy face in sight,
Leaves are falling from the rustling trees,
Hidden inside until morning light,
Leaves fluttering down in the gentle breeze.
Now we know autumn is here to stay,
Until next year, the sunny month of May.

Natalie Cooper (14)
Blurton High School

Magic Carpet

Magic carpet, oh so bright,
Take me high into the sky at night,
See all the houses dotted below,
As I wander to and fro,
Over deserts, over seas,
Through the forest with its waving trees,
Stars that twinkle, a moon that shines,
Why can't everything be just mine?
The feelings I get from this spectacular view
Are hard to explain, especially to you.
I travel like lightning, I travel like floating snow,
Sometimes high, sometimes low.
I don't want my journey to come to an end,
One more stop, it's only around the bend,
It's my favourite place to stop and view,
The sea waves splash and ripple too.
A smell that lies beneath the sea
Of salt water and sand, what else could it be?
The sun is rising, it's time to go home,
To snuggle down in my bed, which is made from chrome,
To rest my head and sleep tight
Until the next time I want a magical flight.

Michelle Poole (15)
Blurton High School

My Cat - Haiku

Little pink nose and
A soft, fluffy tail, four white
Paws, my cat - Sparrow.

Jordan Diskin (14)
Blurton High School

Predator

Lurking in tall stalks of grass
Still, she is a statue, as quiet as a mouse.
As slow as a snail the time does pass,
For the cheetah has strayed from her house.

She edges closer to her prey,
Her ears pointed and alert;
A meal doesn't come every day,
It is vital that she doesn't get hurt.

The prey twitches as it senses danger,
The cheetah is ready to attack.
To the prey, the predator is no stranger
As it stumbles back.

The cheetah knows the time has come,
She is ready to pounce and endeavour,
The victim flees as it knows what it may become,
The cheetah's hunger is stronger than ever.

With a jolt of energy her legs spring her forward,
Her paws pound powerfully along the ground.
She is but an inch away from her prey,
Her solid jaws dig in; the hunt is over.

Chantel Kaur (15)
Blurton High School

Love

Love is like a lump of gold,
Hard to have and hard to hold.
Of all the people I've ever met,
You're the one I can't forget.
So come with me and look above
And see the stars shine with love.
This is the way to stay forever,
Just you and me in hand together.

Charlotte Woodward (15)
Blurton High School

Something In The Night

There is something bright
That glows in the dark night.
It is very big and round
And never goes down and touches the ground.
It shines all through the night
And gives off a bright light.

It seems so white,
As it glistens in the night.
You will never see it during the day,
But wait 'til night and look its way.
This shining light is called the moon,
Look out of the window when it's dark
And you will see it soon.

Kelly Brindley (14)
Blurton High School

Love

Love is a powerful thing that conquers all,
Even in times of despair, love can leave you standing tall.
Love can tell between truth and lie,
Love can be the smile in someone's eye.
Love is exquisite, love is unique,
It happens so fast, it barely leaves you time to think.
Love is in a thousand faces,
Love can happen in a million places.
Love is cruel, love is kind,
Love can two people bind.
Love is unpredictable, it can happen anywhere,
But at the end of the day, be thankful it's there.

Emma Harris (14)
Blurton High School

Wishing Upon A Star

Flecks of glitter
Twinkling high,
The glistening stars
Shine in the sky.
I make a wish
And hope it comes true,
As you watch over me,
All the night through.

Sarah Brennan (14)
Blurton High School

Ten Things Found In Shrek's Pocket

A hair of a donkey,
Six grey slugs,
A pig's eyeball,
Dinner for tomorrow,
Half a pound of mud,
A dirty ear cleaner,
A bill for corrupting children's minds,
A death wish from the local council,
Two dead caterpillars
And an eight-year-old fish.

Zara Owen (11)
Maryhill High School

Dark

Dark is the horrifying coldness,
Dark is the blackness of the sky,
Dark is the shivering winterness,
Dark is the time to cry.

Jacob Woolhouse (11)
Maryhill High School

Autumn

The flowers will start to die,
When the birds start to cry.
The leaves swirl around and around,
Then they gently hit the ground.
Bears will go to sleep,
But the flowers will weep.
Winter is nearly here,
So the robins begin to cheer.
The night comes earlier,
As it's nearly a new year.

Jordan Rigby (12)
Maryhill High School

Space

Black holes, wormholes, twinkling stars,
UFOs and even Mars,
Universe and Milky Way,
All these things are here today,
All these things unrealistic,
Space is so, so very mystic.
All these things I must be dreaming . . .
I was . . . it was my eye deceiving.

Alex Gould (11)
Maryhill High School

My First Day At Maryhill

As I was walking through the gate,
I just knew I was really late.
What if I got terribly lost?
How much do the dinners cost?
At the end of the day,
I realised it was OK,
And now I love Maryhill!

Francesca Lascelles (11)
Maryhill High School

Midnight

It was the middle of the night
And nothing stirred at all.
Everyone was fast asleep,
Then a sound came from the hall.

Up jumped the little girl
To see what it was,
Crept down the creaky stairs
And out of the wooden door.

Everywhere was as white as snow,
Looked like Jack Frost was there that night.
It was freezing cold, she was frightened,
And nobody was in sight.

Then she heard that noise again,
What could it have been?
Then she saw 20 foxes on the grass,
She couldn't believe what she'd seen.

Then she ran back inside
And up to her nice, warm bed,
She got inside and went to sleep,
But the sound was still in her head.

Harriet Mullington (12)
Maryhill High School

The Haunted House

One night when the moon is full,
Ghouls come out to scare you all.
A wolf is howling at the silver ball
Outside the great hall.

Welcome to the haunted house
And the curse of the giant mouse.
Lastly the disgusting woodlouse,
Welcome to the haunted house.

Kieran Walker (11)
Maryhill High School

The Winter Storm

When I woke up this morning, I was surprised to see
Icicles hanging from every tree.
I walked down the stairs and admired the snow,
I started to get into the Christmas flow.
I opened the curtains and stared at the sight,
I wished for Christmas to come, with all my might.

The day grew lighter as I stared outside,
I felt my heart fill up with Christmas pride.
I dressed up warm and went into the cold,
I started to play, I hoped I would never get old.
The wind picked up and the snow whirled around,
Everyone began to shout extremely loud.
It was a *blizzard* closing in,
Everyone started to make an even louder din.

I ran inside and locked the door,
Then I collapsed onto the cold, tiled floor.
The snow splatted on the windowpane,
Then I heard barking, it was Alf, our Great Dane.
I stood up quite slow,
As I recovered from the icy blow.
The snow was quite deep
And was all piled in heaps.

I went upstairs to wake Mum and Dad,
I thought about all the past Christmases I had, had.
I felt excited, Christmas Day was near,
I opened the door then my heart filled with fear.
What happens if the presents don't come?
I reassured myself and began to feel less numb.
Christmas is near!

Heather Porter (12)
Maryhill High School

A Dragon

In a town hundreds of miles away,
Where children were out at play,
There lived a monster so fierce
That the poor king was in tears.
They fed that beast so tall,
With a flock of sheep and more!
But one day in this town,
The number of sheep went down.
All the sheep had gone,
It looked like the dragon had won.
But, oh no! The king wanted to carry on.
He read out a decree,
But the men cried out in a plea.
You see, this decree
Said to kill all girls (like me!)
So now when you go to this town,
It looks a bit of a clown!
The men look a bit down,
Because the girls have gone!

Lisa Stephenson (11)
Maryhill High School

A Recipe For A Wizard

Take a pointed hat,
A pinch of magic,
A crushed wand,
Mix them together in a simmering cauldron.
Then add a black cat,
A crushed rat's guts,
A chopped pumpkin,
Leave in an evil professor,
Then your wizard will appear.

Samantha Jordan (11)
Maryhill High School

Bonfire Night

Bright fireworks in the sky,
Bright, bright fireworks.
Lovely fireworks in the sky,
Lovely, lovely fireworks.

Roaring fires in the night,
Roaring, roaring fires.
Glowing fires in the night,
Glowing, glowing fires.

Sparkling sparklers in the sky,
Sparkling, sparkling sparklers.
Colourful sparklers in the sky,
Colourful, colourful sparklers.

Laughing children in the night,
Laughing, laughing children.
Happy children in the night,
Happy, happy children.

Joshua Ellis (11)
Maryhill High School

A Recipe For An Alien

First take the eyes of a newt and boil until bubbling,
Add the tentacles of a bumblebee,
Stir in some green mould,
Slice up some bats' wings,
Add the sliced-up bats' wings,
Simmer for five minutes.
Take a pinch of hatred and add,
Mix your mixture,
Take a handful of scary powder
And cook for three hours.
Leave to set in a cool, damp place,
And you will have your alien!

Jessica Gallimore (11)
Maryhill High School

Recipe For A Wizard

Sprinkle in some wisdom,
A pinch of courage too,
Simmer gently through a sieve,
The mixture should turn blue.

Roast some magic from within,
Grill some grey goats' hair,
Add these ingredients to the bowl,
Take a sip if you dare!

Boil some stars fresh from the sky,
Pour in some shining wisdom,
Fry the mixture before it sets,
Place it in a place on high.

After, approach the mixture,
Be careful as you go,
Don't run towards it, say a word,
Just walk very slow.

The final package should be great,
Not a lurking ghost, or a wicked witch full of hate,
But a kind and magical wizard.

Nicola Belfield (11)
Maryhill High School

Hallowe'en

H aunted forest, spooky and still
A bandoned house where nothing sleeps
L ingering smell stirs and creeps
L ittle girl screams and shrieks
O pen gates let unwelcome visitors in
W inding staircases, up she creeps
E choing voices, life-like shrieks
E veryone sleeps while she creeps
N ot everyone sleeps on Hallowe'en,
    some wander, while others dream.

Bethany Bowker (11)
Maryhill High School

What Do You Get When You Mix A Witch With A Teacher?

When you mix a witch with a teacher,
We all know you'll get a very ugly creature!
Teachers you hate,
Witches use you as bait!
What will you get?
It'll sure be something you won't forget!
Horror will break,
Be scared, for goodness sake!
Schools are most affected,
Everyone must be protected!
There is something we need to say,
Teachers are witches anyway!

Sam Harris (12)
Maryhill High School

Ten Things Found In An Athlete's Pocket

A piece of dead skin,
A golden medal for her or him,
A knotted-up shoelace from his shoe,
A picture of *oh!* I won't tell you.
A leaking pen from signing a script,
A piece of paper that seems to be ripped,
A bit of his old school tie,
A scary book that made him cry,
A pair of sunglasses with a scratch,
A pair of old shorts,
Repaired with a patch.

Megan Booth (11)
Maryhill High School

A Recipe For A . . . Wizard!

A
Spoon
Full of
Wisdom. A
Handful of stars.
A pointy top hat
And a little black cat.
A teardrop of love. A kiss
Of tender care. A wish or three,
Then fill him with glee, mix them all up,
What do you see? And don't forget the magic!
And there he will be!

Darrien Lowe (12)
Maryhill High School

A Recipe For A Teacher

First heat the oven to gas mark six,
Add a pencil case to a pot of boiling water,
Pour in a jug of anger,
Throw in a monkey's brain for cleverness,
Whisk in a pinch of pencil sharpenings,
Add a text book from any subject,
Mix in a chocolate frog for kindness.
Cook in the oven for half an hour,
Leave to cool in a classroom for two days.
Sprinkle on a handful of helpfulness,
And on the third day, your teacher will be ready.

Daniel Polles (11)
Maryhill High School

Wintertime!

I stood there
In the middle of the street,
Watching the snow fall
And people greet.

It was cold.
I watched all the children play outside,
Should I go to bed?
I could not decide.

I walked along,
Hearing the snow crunch under my feet.
I went in the park and took a seat.

Gemma Hawkins (11)
Maryhill High School

Cats

Cats are always sleeping,
For food they're begging and weeping.
They always want to play,
But when you do, they hiss and run away.

Cats are always in a mood
And they hate other cats stealing their food.
They sit at the door for it to be opened by you,
Then still sit there deciding what to do!

Cats are annoying, really they are,
But to me, my cat's still a star.

Jessica Bamford (11)
Maryhill High School

A Recipe For A Vampire

Pour in the black of the night,
Slice in the impatience of a child,
Stir the screams of a girl,
Boil the fangs of a rattlesnake,
Mix the paleness of a blank wall,
Fry the wings of a bat,
Sprinkle on a little hate,
Bake until shrieking.
Leave for a night,
Remember to lock your doors and windows!

Merecedes Blakemore (11)
Maryhill High School

Waiting!

Waiting for death
Or waiting for life

Waiting for good times
Or waiting for strife

All different things
To think of

To know
So many questions

To learn and to grow
Death is coming

It's waiting for you
But it's not death

It's in life what you do
So make the most of life while it's here
One day, when it's gone, there'll be nothing but tears.

Emily Clowes (13)
Painsley Catholic High School

My Mind

My mind is like a blob of goo,
Thoughts enter my head like
Pictures enter my eyes.
Homework is like a big weight
That you have to carry everywhere.
Teachers are like slave drivers,
You have to do what they say.
School is boring,
It is like watching paint dry.
School is like an unwanted present
That you have to put up with.
Homework is like a big black cloud,
Trying to eat me.
My mind is like a blob of goo.

George Hunt (12)
Painsley Catholic High School

My Mind

My mind is like a bog roll, always thick, very useful.
Thoughts enter my head like a reoccurring roundabout,
Round and round, gears clicking, but nothing's sticking.
I think teachers are like steamrollers,
They never stop and need children to fuel them.
My thoughts turn to mushy peas when
They get crammed into a tiny grey box in my head.
I wonder about those little grey men in space,
And when they are planning to kidnap us.
My mind drifts to food, yummy, scrummy food.
Thoughts spring into my mind like a jack-in-the-box,
You never know when it's coming.
My mind is like a bog roll, always thick, very useful.

Jade Beaumont (12)
Painsley Catholic High School

Winds Of Destruction

America was where it swept towards,
As people ran in their hordes.
The hurricane was sure to hit the land,
Like someone with a powerful hand.

The hurricane charged towards the coast
Of the country which would be its host.
Crash went the waves as they crushed the shore,
But Hurricane Francis still had more.

The traffic built up on the main freeway,
As panic swept, they could not stay.
Their houses boarded with screw and nail,
To protect against the ferocious gale.

Of churning cloud the sky was full,
Trampling homes, this raging bull
Marched inland from west to east,
An uncontrolled, vicious beast.

And so it went, soon came, soon passed,
Trees bent, roofs off, buildings smashed.
No power on, the land in pain,
This was this year's worst hurricane.

Hannah Walton (13)
Painsley Catholic High School

Teachers

My mind is like a prison,
Each cell is hard to remember.
Teachers are like lightning,
You never know when they're going to strike.
Teachers are like birds,
They never shut up.
Teachers are like dictionaries,
They always know everything.
My mind is like a prison,
Each cell is hard to remember.

Alicia Starkey (12)
Painsley Catholic High School

Monster's Den

```
                        Churn.
                  Stomach    The air
                     My          became filled
                   Felt             with screaming
                    I                  cries
                  Soon              and most
                  And          were saying
                 Turn,       their last
                 And          goodbyes!
                 Twist            And as the ride went
                 To              round and round,
                Began                I felt I was
                Ride              falling to the ground.
                The             Sickening jolts
               Eyes,              and
                        squirming bends,
            My      it seemed this ride
           Before            would never end!
           Flash     But as it came to a sudden stop,
           To               I felt my temporary high
          Seemed        go flop!
          Life         So
          My            as
          Skies,       soon as
          The             the
          Into          monster
         Fired           let
         Was            me
         I                  out of his den,
        As                   I ran back round to the queue
       again!
```

Jade Latham (14)
Painsley Catholic High School

The World Is Always Changing

The world is always changing,
It seems to spin around me.
It encloses me in a box; which nobody else can see.

Feeling kind of happy,
I want to scream and shout.
Why won't somebody tell me, what this life is meant to be about?

I'm feeling down and out these days,
Trying to find a way.
I need a path to guide me in what I do and say.

Coming to a climax now,
It's not all plain black and blue.
How can anything in this world, in this, in me, be true?

The world is always changing,
It seems to spin around me.
It encloses me in a box; which nobody else can see.

Hannah Smith (13)
Painsley Catholic High School

Minds

My mind is as heavy as a feather
Because I am not that brainy.

I think homework is like a black cloud
Because it follows me everywhere.

I think watching TV is as funny
As a laughing clown.

I think about playing on my PS2
It is as good as playing football.

I think about my mum,
She is as lovely as a box of chocolates.

Thoughts enter my mind like a rocket.

Oliver Bateman (12)
Painsley Catholic High School

Place A Dove

I look around and meet his eye,
He'll never be mine no matter how hard I try.
It feels like my world is about to end,
My heart seems impossible to ever mend.

I forget my fears with every touch,
I've never been in love, at least not this much.
I think to myself, I've got myself in deep,
All my thoughts are about him, I can't even sleep.

I sit and stare at him in class,
Hoping this lesson will quickly pass.
Actually, I wish that I could die,
So in my hollow grave I could peacefully lie.

I see him kissing a girl in the park,
I think he is deliberately making his mark.
I arrive home in floods of tears,
I feel like crying for millions of years.

So here I sit on my bedroom floor,
Pain rushing through me more and more.
I lift the bottle full of pills,
One by one I swallow, sending my body chills.

The bottle is empty, I'm not yet dead,
So I grip my fingers round a knife instead.
I stab my wrists, cutting deep,
I'm shaking all over, my body is weak.

I'm lying here in a pool of blood,
I suddenly collapse, my head falls with a thud.
Now I scrawl the words, 'I love you Mum,
And I'm sorry, to this end it has come'.

Everyone, I'm sorry, please don't cry for me,
Just think this is how I wanted it to be.
And on my grave, please place a dove,
Then in your heart remember, I died for love.

Rosie Shenton (13)
Painsley Catholic High School

Fox Hunting Poem

Black-capped riders,
Red coats, blazing against a watery sky,
Low lying mists through valleys sweep,
Cold breath spiralling like ghostly vespers.

Blow, blow, blow the horn,
The wailing echo as the master calls,
Drink from the cups, drain the glass,
Feel the burning spirit flow.

Hoar frosts sit on wintry boughs,
Fallen gates at awkward angles lie,
Water-filled ruts, frozen hard, hooves slipping, sliding,
Thick ice zigzag cracking.

The furtive fox, ears laid flat, eyes wide open, pupils glaring,
Hunched low down, belly dragging,
Draw down deep, nostrils flaring,
Exhaled air warm and wet, hanging like fog in the still cold air.

Creeping, crawling to get away,
Using hedge and hollow, copse and furrow,
Barking, howling the hounds draw nearer,
Galloping horses, a blood fuelled throng.

Escape, escape use the ground,
The shrill metal calling the hunter's song,
The ultimate game, the misled hound.

Muscles rippling, burning, aching,
Lungs expand, claw in the air, the cold chill bites,
No respite, no rest, the contest prolonged.

Hounds close by, ears flapping,
No more running, hiding, evading,
Deep bold braying calling for the cull,
Time for a final stand.

Teeth bared, bold and white, no more fear dispelled for the fight,
One on many a desperate charge,
Bite, bite, bite, tooth and claw,
Wounding, slashing, the end is near.

Open wounds down to the bone,
Hot blood flows onto the frozen ground,
The hunt is over, the deed is done,
The fox is dead,
The pain is gone.

Chloe Worrall (13)
Painsley Catholic High School

The Natural World

The autumn wind throws about his long and graceful gown,
As he plays, his hair rustles the entwined fingers of the trees
And a golden blanket of crispy leaves dances
Around together, as he whirls them round and round.
Tall giants shed their leaves like hair and all around lie
Peaceful mountains of golden-brown bliss,
Undisturbed by the dancing king.

The merry squirrel hops and jumps from tree to tree
As happy as the gleaming autumn sun
And as graceful as a swan,
For he knows his hibernation is fast coming and
He needs all fruitful treasures that the shedding trees can bear.
Sun's bright yellow rays spread across the sky
And catch every crystal dewdrop that hangs from
The little wilting old ladies that swing softly in the meadow.

The princess of the sky is changing,
Her cloak, once a sapphire summer blue,
Now a feathery, misty orange,
As she grows older and her majestic colours become duller.
A full moon blooms in autumn night and the stars shine,
Like twinkling diamonds on a gossamer, black, velvet gown.

Anastasia Donaldson (13)
Painsley Catholic High School

A Poem For A Poet In Need

Spending his time thinking,
He doesn't know what to do!
He sits and thinks and thinks and thinks and thinks,
He doesn't have a clue.

He thinks up an idea
And writes it on a sheet,
He thinks what things are related to this,
He thinks of a good beat.

He starts off his poem,
He wants to do it quick.
He's stuck. What rhymes with quality?
Then he suddenly clicks.

He uses his English skills
That Mrs Mitchell taught him.
'My poem doesn't have to rhyme!
Why was I so dim?

I can use some similes,
Or a metaphor instead.
I can use emotive language,'
He starts to use his head.

He uses his techniques,
It's starting to work well,
He remembers English lessons,
The lessons she used to tell.

He finishes his poem,
The poem is very nice!
It's based on his English lessons
And Mrs Mitchell's advice.

English teachers are the best,
They help you in later days.
This is the moral of the poem,
Teachers have their little ways.

Elita Unyolo (13)
Painsley Catholic High School

Ken Bigley

This must be torture of the human race,
With terror stricken all over his face.
They took him away
On that terrible day.

He couldn't escape Iraq.

His eyes grew lifeless with no desire,
His face drew cold by a gunshot fire.
They sent Blair a message when they took him away,
They'd already killed two, with a third on the way.

He couldn't escape Iraq.

They requested women from out of jail,
Requested it through the video mail.
In that video we all saw Ken,
Surrounded by those terrorist men.

He couldn't escape from Iraq.

In all this mess, what happened to Blair?
Such a great mind wasted, seems so unfair.
So Ken pleads for his life with all his might,
With this terrorist torture it isn't right.

He couldn't escape from Iraq.

Stacey Black (13)
Painsley Catholic High School

Cruelty To Children

Try to lend a helping hand
To show that you understand.
Try to create a happy atmosphere
To help the children lose their fear.

Bruised and battered to a pulp,
Give some pennies to help them bunk.
In a place that's safe and warm
Like a tiny baby before it's born.

Cruelty to children happened frequently,
Behind closed doors they abuse them secretly.
Show people that you know
Cruelty to children has got to go.

Bang! Another child has been badly hurt,
Help them now, before their spirit deserts.
Just give an afternoon a week
To help the poor bruised children sleep.

Think of all the pain they have,
Just as if they're a punching bag.
Wind whistles through the night
When the children are deep in fright.

Think of a big bare chair that doesn't move all day,
It's just like children too scared to play.
Children are like stars in the night,
Shining bright; sleeping softly, sound and tight.

The sun is a fireball in the sky when
Then it starts all over again.
From dawn till dusk and every hour
The children like pups learn to cower.

The children live from day to day
Hoping that it will go away.
All they want is a loving smile
From their parents once in a while.

Once the bright sun has gone to sleep
You can hear the children weep.
So please help stop and start to nurture
For these poor children are our future.

Hayley Finney (13)
Painsley Catholic High School

Seasons In My Mind

Happiness filled the room,
My mind said, summer's here,
Fresh-baked loaves of golden bread,
The sun whispers in my ear.

Get up, get dressed,
Shine in the sun,
But I stop, stand still and stare.
Summer's gone and autumn's come.

Crisp leaves crunching, munching,
Getting louder, my head is banging.
Which way should I go?
I'm stuck in a web, which needs untangling.

But then all is calm,
Quiet, serene and still,
Harmonising colours
As winter settles in.

The seasons in my mind
Are what I am and will be.
All that's left is spring,
I wonder what I'll see?

Jessica Cooper (13)
Painsley Catholic High School

The Fox

The fox of the moonlit sky
Runs away from the hunter's cry.
The hounds whose teeth often bare
Try to give the fox a heck of a scare.
Quickly, the fox runs through a tree's root
Trying to give the hunter the boot.
The fox runs as swift as a hare
Whereas the hunters couldn't really care,
Because they hadn't made a kill,
Their score was just plain, old nil.

Many times the fox has luckily fled
And managed to make its winter bed,
This time will the fox prevail,
Or will the fox just sooner fail?
The fox's tail swishes from side to side,
Making it wave in pride.
The long fine tail which is always bright
Keeps the fox's courage up all day and night.
Its tail is as colourful as the autumn leaves
Which swirl around in the autumn breeze.

The majestic fox who runs with might
Is not just about to give up the fight,
The hounds and huntsmen suddenly exceed,
But the fox too picks up speed.
Mr Fox who runs over branches and leaves
Runs so fast that the hounds can't breathe.
The hounds are like soldiers, working for food,
Never stopping, not a change in mood.
The huntsmen are the leaders, who just boss,
They are always angry and always get cross.

The hounds followed the fox through every turn
Whereas the poor little fox's feet did burn.
The fox's life had been cruel and unfair,
Mainly because he's been chased everywhere.
The experienced expert fox knew the way,
When younger he had come here to play.
His father and mother were killed by the huntsmen
Just for stealthily stealing a fat juicy hen
The hounds ripped them apart like a piece of card
And left the fox emotionally scarred.

Through forest and open fields the fox did run,
The death chase had not long begun.
Then they came to a barbed wire fence,
All the fox could do was tense.
He jumped over and his courage rose high,
He felt like a bird flying in the sky.
Whereas behind he heard a great *splash!*
He saw that a man had fell and had a gash.
The hunt was soon over, although it had just begun,
The fearless fox, was now free to play and run.

Matthew Thompson (13)
Painsley Catholic High School

J R R Tolkien

J R R Tolkien he's my star,
Because he wrote the best story by far.
From the dwarfish Moria Gate,
To Mordor where all evil awaits.
From Arathorn
To Aragorn.
From Lothlorien
To Ithilien.
Oh! Come on, you must've guessed!
It's 'The Lord of the Rings'
Without a doubt the best.

Steven Ward (11)
Painsley Catholic High School

As The Day Crawls Slowly Into Night

As the day crawls slowly into night
I snuggle up in my rags, right up tight,
Not letting warmth escape me, that would be bad,
But I'm comfy, warm and sleepy on this concrete slab.
I'm sleeping outside a great, fantastic, brilliant mall,
Watching people go home in cars, the family's dog and all.
I'm very sad watching this, for they have a place to go,
Whereas I'm just lying here, waiting for the snow.

At ten o'clock the Christmas lights go out and I'm bathed in black,
I cannot see my fingers, they are cold and that's a fact.
I feel something cold fall gently on my nose,
I touch it, it melts, and here comes the snow.
'It's heavy tonight,' I heard some people say,
And in the snow tomorrow they will laugh and play.
Yet they have got a bed, a shelter for their head,
Whereas I'm just waiting here, almost close to death.

More snow is falling, heavier now; I'm shivering a lot,
My body is cold, my nose blocked, my eyes very bloodshot.
My toes, what toes? I try to feel them with my might,
But I can't, woe is me! It's the start of cruel frostbite.
The snow is up to my waist; I'm surely close to death,
My feet are numb and my chest is sharp with each breath.
Three hours later from then, the snow is up to my head,
I cannot breathe any longer now, I fall asleep . . . dead.

Jessica Wilson (13)
Painsley Catholic High School

My Pet Polly

My cat and I have so much fun,
She brightens my day just like the sun.
I groom her every night and day,
She's my best friend, hip, hip, hooray!

She's my little princess, her name is Polly,
She chases her tail; she's such a wally.
Once she got stuck up a tree,
But then she climbed back down to me.

She loves me lots and I love her,
I scratch her ears and hear her purr.
She looks at me with big green eyes,
And squeaks a miaow, 'Come here,' she cries.

If you pull her tail she will not mind,
She will forgive you, she is so kind
She jumps on your knee and falls asleep,
And when she wakes up, off she will leap.

She cheers me up when I am down,
She makes me laugh; she's such a clown.
She is so cute and ever so pretty,
She's my little girl, my little kitty!

Amy Fallows (13)
Painsley Catholic High School

Churchill

C raftily led the enemy on,
H eadstrong, never gave up,
U nderrated by some,
R eady to command at all times,
C unning, always had a plan,
H ated losing,
I ntelligent, always knew what to do,
L eader at all times,
L oyal to England, even when under fire.

James Drew (12)
Painsley Catholic High School

Down The Catwalk

Rush, rush, rush, through the traffic,
To get to the show, but it's still manic,
Straight to dressing
There's no messing
We've got to be ready on time,
We are putting reputations on the line,
As we get ready, our hair and make-up done,
It's time to get dressed, oh what fun,
One, two, three, the countdown goes,
Everyone's nervous perhaps it shows,
Click, click, click, flash, flash, flash,
The pictures are sold to mags for cash,
Gliding down the catwalk, like floating on air,
Not to look, but allowed to stare,
Time to come off, cannot stay, been pushed to the maxi,
Just one word . . . *taxi!*

Nicola Cornwall (13)
Painsley Catholic High School

My Mind

My mind is like footsteps following my every move.
My eyes start to rise, homework is the first thing that enters my mind.
Have I done it? Is it right?
My mind starts to drift on and on elsewhere.
Friends are the next thing that creeps into my mind
They often are like roses, sweet-smelling and best friends,
But they turn to thorns, stabbing me in the back.
Food, I love it, it's yummy to the bone,
It's like it gives me a thrill, rumbling in my tummy.
Family are the next thing that springs into my mind.
They're like devils nagging on my side,
But then they turn to angels saving my every fall.
My mind is like footsteps following my every move.

Melissa Nash (12)
Painsley Catholic High School

My Mind

My mind always thinks about football
Football is my favourite sport
I like it because it's fun.
In different countries most people play football
More than 50 percent of the girls or women play football.

In football I hate one thing, when people spit at each other
And they say those dirty words at each other
But it's not nice to say those.
Sometimes you might get punished because of that word you said,
If you get a red card you will have two weeks of no football.

Soccer makes people crazy, even at home,
I have football games and most of the time I spend
                    my day only playing football
Because I think I was meant for it.
Also soccer is one of the games which pays the most money.

In soccer you also have to know the rules
Because if you do not know the rules you won't be able to play it.
Most people say, 'I can play football'
But if you ask them one rule in soccer they don't even know one.

My favourite country in football is England,
And my favourite club is Real Madrid.

Tapiwa Sibanda (12)
Painsley Catholic High School

Racism

Racism is a powerful word,
When I hear it I feel my emotions get stirred
As violently as a hurricane,
A fist pounding, thundering in my brain.

Why be scared of someone's skin?
That's not as important as what's within,
A person's heart,
So be smart,
Lead racism out the door.

We don't need to compare until one
Group comes out on top.
All this pathetic ignorance just has to stop,
So howl like a hungry hound
Until old man racism is no longer around.

Sport is leading by example,
Under its feet racism is trampled,
So let's all follow in its lead
Giving people the chances they deserve and need.

So, you see, racism is a mug's game,
Why can't we treat each other the same?
Then the world would be a huge melting pot
Where the wrapping we come in, matters not one jot.

Matthew Wheatley (14)
Painsley Catholic High School

Fashion Poem

I am standing in the mall
On a very busy day.
The fashions change like seasons,
What fabulous fashion will I see?

Looking round what do I see?
The window display is like a rainbow,
Red, yellow, orange and brown,
Autumn colours are fashion today.

I look around at the dazzling fashions,
Jumpers, jackets and pretty skirts.
Zip goes my new fashion dress
And the hat sits on my head like a tea cosy.
The new fashions sell so quickly.

Looking in the shops for something nice,
The diamond necklace is a friend to me.
The stripy scarf waves to me,
Fashion is an accessory.

My new polo neck surrounds me like a comfortable cat
And my jacket is a piece of cloth with a heater in.
Oh fashion grows so quickly.

Olivia Shenton (13)
Painsley Catholic High School

The Hurricane

The suspense was building,
The tension was mounting,
The terror of people had
Reached a brand new climax.

It was only a matter of time before,
This atrocious, horrific, unruly beast,
Was to claim the lives of many,
Everyone knew its deadly path.

Then, suddenly there was an almighty howl,
The trees swayed and the trunks shook,
The rain crashed to the floor,
And the debris flew across the road.

Roofs were ripped off the houses,
Cars lifted effortlessly off the ground,
Glass smashed in seconds,
Lamp posts snapped like twigs.

The hurricane had arrived.

Helen Chesworth (14)
Painsley Catholic High School

What I Have To Put Up With

My mum is the best but she doesn't like it if you make a mess,
The reason for this is she can't give it a miss.

My dad is cool but embarrassing when he brings me to school,
I just want to lock him up in his room.

My sister's cute,
But sometimes she gets on my boot.

My brother is mean, when he pinches me I scream,
He is as mean as a dumping machine.

As for me I'm perfect and could never be any better,
Because when I'm the best I am better than all the rest.

Jenna Forrester (11)
Painsley Catholic High School

Animal Cruelty

People of England, people of Ireland come and join
Me now up high,
Help me stop this thing
Which goes on all the time.

Why do you do this, what have they done to you?
They won't harm you,
They just want love from you,
So just let them have your love.

Why would you keep them in and kill them
In that appalling heavy home of yours
With those huge teeth that come onto them
Like teeth?

Nice as pies,
Harmful as a bee,
Why would you do this to them?
They're yours to keep!

You're always thrashing and crashing them about
With your faces like thunder.
People wouldn't treat you like you treat them
So let's think about it, be nice.

People of England, people of Ireland come join
Me now up high,
Help me stop this thing
Which goes on all the time.

James Sellers (13)
Painsley Catholic High School

Football Poem

Football is a crazy game
But the big scam is the prices,
The stadium needs filling
So lower the prices!

Players get paid thousands
But why do fans pay so much?
The stadium would be full
If the costs were kicked into touch.

The merchandise is expensive,
A ticket can cost £30.
Make it all cheaper please,
Come on, hear our sounds.

Programmes, pies, pints and peas,
It all costs too much cash.
Make the food cheaper please
Or there'll be a fans' backlash.

Players move to other clubs
Where they can earn more money.
See your team crash down the league
Then watching them is not funny.

The stadium can be hell,
It feels so cold and gloomy,
As if the sun is crying
And it hides behind clouds looming.

But when you win
There's no feeling like it,
It's as if the sun is beaming.
You leave the ground
With a spring in your step,
Proud to be wearing your kit.

Simon Bostock (14)
Painsley Catholic High School

Chip, Chop

Chip, chop, chip and chop
Is the sound heard around.
The rainforest floor
Is covered with gore.
A massacre takes place
Every day of every year.

The trees have fallen
All around, begging for breath.
They weep with sorrow,
They will die tomorrow,
Turned to paper, tables and chairs
But for them, no one cares.

Animals run in fear and fright
Like scared little children in the night;
Their homes destroyed,
The killer employed,
Mother and child separated
For things to be created.

Sounds like a thunder slash!
As a tree falls down upon a tribe,
Fires start and children cry
As their parents have just died.
The lives of many hell
To make many things, for many to sell.

So I say stop this now
Like a good man would.
Great, gorgeous giant trees,
Animals, plants, birds and bees
As whining children beg and please,
Are killed upon their treasured homes
And this we must seize!

Edward Frith (13)
Painsley Catholic High School

Individuality

People, people everywhere
But no one stops to think,
Why everybody everywhere
Is so obsessed with pink!

Pink may be just a colour
But to me it means much more,
It takes away the one thing
That might just link us all.

The one thing we have in common
Is what sets us apart,
For we are all different
Right from the very start.

Why not break free from the mould?
Will the others point and jibe?
If they do, just laugh back,
Don't run away to hide.

Don't let fashion be your prison,
Don't let it rule your life,
Banish pink from whence it came,
Be gone with all that strife.

Maybe pretty pink and baby blue
Is something to hide behind,
But what are you afraid of?
What don't you want to find?

Maybe life is tough,
Beyond all that mascara,
But in fact it's just the same,
If you work a little harder!

Come out from underneath your shell
And this I solemnly swear,
That life is like a dream outside,
It's just getting there!

Crash through those wide barriers,
Take off all that foundation,
You will be tested on the way
But don't give in to temptation.

Who are they to judge you?
And this I cannot see,
How, how you look and dress,
Can be your personality.

Hannah Mundy (14)
Painsley Catholic High School

Fox Hunting

The fox ran so fast it flew,
Not fast enough, the others knew,
The dogs ran close behind
Ready to blow the fox's mind.

The dogs were bears, claws outstretched,
They thrust them deep into the chest.
The master took out a gun,
Boom! the fox exploded like a sun.

'Jolly good show,' the master said,
'Back to the clubhouse for tea and bread!'
Another fox dead and what for?
For them to be stuffed and hung on a door.

The fox was like a poor, bouncing bunny rabbit,
How could man like a devil pick up this habit?
The fox pleaded with man,
We must put this hunting to a ban.

Why do we have to kill?
Can't we leave the foxes to chill?
Fox hunting is like death,
Soon there will be no foxes left!

David Cooke (14)
Painsley Catholic High School

Fox Hunting

All lined up behind the master,
His coat as red as blood.
Tails swishing in excitement,
The horses stand like they should.

Off they go into the gloomy wood,
The day so hot, like the sun is near.
The bright sun shows its angry face,
Foxes look up, full of fear.

The wind then turns as sharp as a knife,
The foxes see the lead man.
His boots as black as a moonless night,
The dogs speed as fast as they can.

The horn so loud, like a shout from God,
The trees block the huntsmen's way.
The hungry hounds get ready for food,
It will be a successful day.

Hounds sniff as they whiff,
The fox they can smell that's near.
They catch the poor thing and let out a bark,
So the huntsmen group can hear.

Bang! In no time the fox is dead,
Lying there as cute as a kitten.
What harm did they do to deserve this torture?
The real bloodsport of Britain!

Emily Davidson (13)
Painsley Catholic High School

Child Abuse

Oh no! It was happening again!
Her dad stormed through demolishing anything in his path,
Screaming her name time and time again.
Help! Help! She cried silently, nowhere to run, not like last time.
Quivering with fear she sat on her bed,
Hoping, wishing, praying she was dead.

But no! Too late!
He's got her, like a cheetah he waited ready to kill.
By her hair he grabbed her, dragging her ruthlessly down the stairs.
She wailed, she bawled, she screamed and crawled
But nothing unlocked his rage-driven grip.

The fear in her eyes as he raised his hand to meet her face,
Was enough to make a grown man sob.
Silently her tears fell onto her T-shirt,
Soon to be covered by the poor girl's blood.

Amy Chesworth (14)
Painsley Catholic High School

Aryton Senna

Aryton Senna, now he was a great mind,
There has never been another quite of his kind,
You may think all he did was race,
However that was not the case,
He was a true born racer at the top of his sport,
His skill so refined and utterly fantastic, no one could ever be taught,
All I ask is why?
Why did he have to die?
Someone so good, a master, a true inspiration,
Following his dreams, his goals, his vocation,
And all I ask is why?
Why did he have to die?

Jacob Bould (15)
Painsley Catholic High School

Unhappy Memories

I remember the 10th of April,
I remember it very well.
It was the year of 1912
And a story I have to tell.

The Titantic's maiden voyage,
People's spirits were sky high.
Waving friends and families off
Was our last farewell, goodbye.

The luxury ocean holiday
Was planned for this great, big ship,
It was to the USA,
An exciting and joyful trip.

We sailed across the ocean,
Entertainment on the way.
We did not know what was coming:
A very fateful day.

It was the eve of the 14th,
The month of April bloom.
We were sailing on quite easily
Despite the dark night's gloom.

Then the ship, she hit an iceberg
In the middle of the sea,
It brought on a great panic,
It was terrible for me.

They brought out all the lifeboats
And sent them down below.
Women and children got first choice
And none of us were slow.

There were not enough lifeboats
To save some people's lives.
It ended in a tragedy
When only 705 survived.

And to this very day
I remember it very well.
It was the year of 1912
And a story I have to tell.

Rebecca Unyolo (12)
Painsley Catholic High School

Smoking!

Whatever you do, don't smoke,
It makes you smell like smoke pouring from a chimney,
It's not a pleasant smell for people around you,
It damages your lungs.

Whatever you do, don't smoke,
It can give people the wrong impression
And make them think you're bad news.
People hiss like a snake at the smell of the smoke.

Whatever you do, don't smoke,
People wearily pass you,
People try to avoid you,
People think you smell like a hideous, raging fire.

Whatever you do, don't smoke,
People think you smell like thick smoke,
People quickly walk past
To get away from the hideous stench.

Whatever you do, don't smoke,
It can shorten your life dramatically.
Whatever you do, don't smoke,
People always think of you covered in a thick, drifting fog.

Thomas Wilcox (13)
Painsley Catholic High School

Fatal Destruction

No one knew but on that day,
Fatal destruction was on the way.
A hurricane was about to hit,
But no one knew the full extent of it.

As Hurricane Francis dawned
The victims in other countries mourned.
The counties had been terrorised,
A natural disaster had ruined their lives.

The disastrous hand of the hurricane
Had suddenly caused so much pain.
The trees were uprooted, the roads were bare,
There were bits of houses everywhere.

But as people tried to get back on track
Another hurricane was coming back.
Their lives were about to be ruined again,
They had to prepare for more fatal destruction.

Danielle Roberts (13)
Painsley Catholic High School

Thomas Edison

Thomas Edison, the great inventor
Was born in 1847.
His work in the field of communications,
Greatly influenced the world in which we live.
Edison made a small transmitter
To increase the volume in Bell's telephone.
The light bulb was one of Edison's inventions,
Each one giving one thousand hours of light.
To produce a rival to gas illumination,
Edison invented the first power station.
Genius is one per cent inspiration
And ninety-nine per cent perspiration.

Isaac Cooke (11)
Painsley Catholic High School

Great Minds

A great mind thinks about others before themselves
And doesn't shelve other's emotions,
They keep your life in motion
Without much devotion.
They take you by the hand
And keep you safe and sound.
They keep you out of trouble
And make sure you're on the double!
They're the ones who keep you spick 'n' span
Without the use of a plan.
They pick you up when you fall,
They make your life such a ball.
They taught you to crawl and then to draw!
You often think that you got the pick of the draw!
But some might say it's just a mother's intuition.

Ben Gascoigne (15)
Painsley Catholic High School

Bill Gates

Bill Gates is a very clever man,
PlayStations and Xbox were his inventions,
Enjoyed by children far and wide,
'We want more!' they desperately cried.

Bill Gates a very affluent man,
Microsoft made him where he is now,
Microsoft was his best invention,
Which brought him wealth and attention.

Bill Gates, computer software giant,
A help for children who need to learn,
Computer technology can help them all,
Information 24 hours on call.

Ben Cartwright (11)
Painsley Catholic High School

Nelson Mandela

White and black,
Black and white,
Two races very much alike.

White and black,
Black and white,
He knew how to put them right.

He stood up tall and spoke aloud,
But this did not impress the white folk's crowd.

Fearfully he sailed to Robben,
Standing alone, his heart was throbbing.

For twenty-six years he kept his beliefs,
Spending his time with robbers and thieves.

Isolation was not the key,
In 1990 he sailed free.

Laura Warrilow (11)
Painsley Catholic High School

A Brief History Of Stephen Hawking

What a guy that Stephen Hawking,
Poor chap, there's no more talking.
Got a computer to speak his thoughts,
So it's obviously the last resort.
He is a clever guy that chap Steve
Gave Einstein a run for his money,
But books on physics, just ain't funny!
So anyway he's sitting there in his chair
Needing total day and night care,
But all in all he's one great chap and mind,
Decided to write a brief history of time.

Siân Metcalf (11)
Painsley Catholic High School

Neil Armstrong

Neil and his crew were very brave men,
They trained day and night to see the moon's light.
He went to the rocket shaking in fright,
But waiting for the time that was right.

He boarded the ship, anxious and ready,
His life on the line, one more time.
The NASA team prepared once again,
To launch into space those three elite men.

Countdown arrived, ten down to one,
The time of the launch arrived then was gone.
The rocket was launched, their journey begun,
Their guiding light was the light from the sun.

For four days and nights they floated in space,
The Americans had won the space race.
Their historic moment arriving quite soon,
As Neil Armstrong became the first man on the moon.

Thomas Brough (11)
Painsley Catholic High School

Thomas Edison

Thomas Edison was an inventive man,
Over powering toil his imagination ran.
Effortlessly he ignited the globe
Making possible the flashing strobe.

Though half-deaf as a boy, excluded from school,
Racing through books proved him no fool.
Genius he claimed was mostly hard work,
Twenty hours a day in his lab he'd lurk.

Lightning travelled down the string of his kite
Enabling us to light the night.
Patents followed in an ever-flowing stream
A rags to riches story of the American dream.

Thomas Harriden (11)
Painsley Catholic High School

Jacqueline Wilson

Jacqueline Wilson, so inspiring,
What witty story will she think of next?
Her books are laughable and shocking,
Jacqueline Wilson, so inspiring.

Jacqueline Wilson, so inspiring,
Her books are intriguing,
It's like they tie a rope around you,
Dragging you in and in and in.

Jacqueline Wilson, so inspiring,
Books so good,
Would you buy them?
I would.

Jacqueline Wilson - best kids author.

Amy Plant (11)
Painsley Catholic High School

Great Steps

N ever had anyone walked on the moon,
E very eye was upon him,
I n his spacecraft he prepared himself for the journey,
L ong was the journey, short the steps.

A s he made a first step down from the craft,
R eady to make a mark in history,
M any watched their TV screens as he
S teadily heaved his heavy boots.
T iny steps for man, huge steps for mankind,
R adios and TV carried the news to all the world,
O verwhelmed with praise.
N o one will be as famous as him,
G ravity defied by man.

Matthew Fone (11)
Painsley Catholic High School

Fashion

Fashion for me,
Fashion for you,
But why so expensive,
What should I do?

If you are tall or thin,
Designer shops pull you in,
With prices so high,
Only for the rich,
I could never afford to buy.

The warm jumpers,
They want to hug me tight,
But at sixty pounds,
My money's gone with a fight.

The price says it's very cheap,
But is it something I will keep,
Buy one, get one free,
Too much choice for me.

I always go to sales,
But become like a red rag to a bull,
Easily frustrated,
When the shops are full.

All customers are vultures,
Eyes as sharp as knives,
A single sapphire jumper
Is ruling their lives.

I quickly grab my change,
As quick as a flash,
With all the heavy change,
I'm out with a zooming dash.

I return home,
As weary as an old goat,
The rain splutters down
And I forgot to buy a coat!

Nicola Regan (13)
Painsley Catholic High School

Ode From An Irate Schoolgirl

I'm known to be a peaceful soul;
By nature, I'm quite placid.
But there's one thing that makes my blood boil
And turns my thoughts to acid -
Why don't all schools have lockers
To store away our bags?
Why do we carry loads all day
And turn our clothes to rags?

Our blazer shoulders soon wear thin,
(Much to our mums' despair)
With all the weight within our bags;
It really isn't fair!
I trudge along to school each day
Lop-sided, heavy-laden,
With manner of burdened donkey
Instead of sweet fair maiden.

In years gone by all pupils had
A desk to call their own,
A place to neatly store their work
At school, not at their home.
But in the 90s all that changed,
'Give them tables!' was the cry.
But I don't think they gave a thought
To the reality for you and I.

For modern resources weigh so much
And course work is essential,
With folders, files and paperwork,
Displaced spines are consequential!
At night I lie tucked in my bed
Like a hedgehog in hibernation,
And try to work out ways to stop
My mum from hyperventilation.

I dream of my bright locker, my saviour, my friend,
Whose arms are open wide
And with a whoosh she welcomes
All my secrets safe inside.
What useful purpose do tables serve?
We put our school bags under -
But in the midst of double maths
We rip our tights asunder!

Yet even though we try so hard
To get the contents right,
We still don't always have our books,
'I took it home last night!'
A locker would solve the problem
And I think I know the way -
Petition Parliament promptly
And let good sense rule the day.

Lindsey Alcock (13)
Painsley Catholic High School

My Dad

Not small, not tall,
My dad has got it all.
A little shiny on top
But that is not a lot.
My dad is warm and loving
And a bit of a pudding.
I love my dad
And that's what counts.
For he is my dad,
A king of the dads,
That's my dad.

Callum O'Rourke (11)
Painsley Catholic High School

William Golding

William Golding wins the Nobel Prize,
For his novel called 'Lord of the Flies'.
With Ralph, Piggy, Simon and Jack,
You can't help but read it from front to back.

Boys on an island, scared and alone
With the absence of a TV or a phone.
With no hope of rescue
They might as well give in,
But don't worry as your ship may soon come in.

Fighting and arguing, will this ever end?
Of course it will, it drives you round the bend.
Then all of a sudden, out of the blue,
In comes a Navy ship to rescue you.

William Golding had a very great mind,
I wish I had one too,
But sadly, I haven't. Do you?

Matthew Hurst (15)
Painsley Catholic High School

Family Life

Considerable and loving are my mum and dad,
Willing to tackle any problems I may have.
My dad is very stylish, sporty and stressed,
With his job being that busy he only wants the best.

Mum is prepared to do most things,
She's affectionate and loving, also my best friend.
Mum is protective over me,
Whilst Dad thinks I should spread my wings a bit.

Together a long time before they had me,
Always out with friends when they were free.
Treasuring the thought of a family one day,
Mum, Dad and I are always meant to be.

Elizabeth Lloyd (11)
Painsley Catholic High School

The Lamb Executioner

Farmer John had a gun under his buckled belt,
Off to the barn to kill the lambs whose lives had just begun.
Shooting wildly, at the lambs, as if no pain he felt,
To farmer John and his son Steve it was just like playground fun.

The dead lamb's mother looked up at John,
With a glaze like fog over her sorrowful eyes.
Why was it that he had to kill her first and newborn child,
It was like her heart had been torn out and left alone to die.

The barn mourned aloud for the lost little lambs,
As the silence crept over the land.
How was it that their lives were taken,
By a sweat-filled human hand?

We all know this is farmer John's fault,
With his nose in the air like he rules us all.
But soon on this farm, revenge will be sweet
And no more lambs will be made into meat.

When you see that lamb in an ocean deep freezer,
Exchange it for some meatless Spam.
Imagine your family frozen and packages
And think again before you eat lamb.

Emma Jackson (13)
Painsley Catholic High School

Miaow

They go miaow when they are hungry.
They go miaow when they are thirsty.
They go miaow when they want a fuss.
They go miaow when they are happy.
They go miaow when they are sad.
They go miaow as they lick you.
They go miaow when they stand outside,
Wanting to come in,
As miaowing is what cats do!

Eleanna Parkinson (11)
Painsley Catholic High School

Simply The Best!

I love my mum,
She is great,
She cooks, cleans and washes up,
But she's never early, always late.

I love my dad,
He's the best,
He's fun, he laughs, he even smiles,
He never feels like a quest.

My mum and dad get me what I want,
Because they are so kind,
That is why I'm so nice,
Because they put stuff in my mind.

My family are so fun,
They make me feel happy when I'm dull,
If there's something wrong,
They always make the call.

Alisha White (11)
Painsley Catholic High School

Sir Isaac Newton

Sir Isaac Newton,
It must be said,
Made a great discovery,
By being hit on the head.

'Eureka,' he exclaimed
While sitting under a tree.
'It must be gravity which made
This apple fall on me.'

So the theory is,
He said with a frown,
'What goes up,
Must come down.'

Matt Capper (15)
Painsley Catholic High School

An Inspiration

Rain splatters on the soft ground,
Oozing yellow snakes scatter across the mire,
Trickling like miniature waterfalls
Down into the trenches.

There the soldiers sit,
Kneeling in rivers of mud,
Drops of rain splashing all around,
The chill, freezing to the bones.

Breath turns to mist in the cold air,
An apprehensive silence is broken only by the patter
And splash of raindrops,
Whispers travel along the trench.

The Germans were gone.

Still the world remembers,
The great minds that fought for us,
Some giving their lives,
Others living with the horror of war.

For a great mind can be anything,
A genius,
An influence,
An inspiration.

Alice Jarvis (15)
Painsley Catholic High School

My Neil Armstrong Poem

N eil was the first man on the moon in 1966.
E cstatic, yet trembling,
I ntelligent and brave
L ike no one before him, first man on the moon.

A rmed with his rocket,
R aced to the moon,
M ovies had only dreamed
S uch an adventure.
T he man began to count down,
R eady, steady, go.
O nly time to make adjustments,
N eil was feeling scared and anxious,
G o, go, go.

Gareth Mycock (13)
Painsley Catholic High School

The Great Mind Of J K Rowling

J K Rowling has a magical mind,
This amazing author is one of a kind.
She writes of adventures that set out to deceive
And tells about tales that you wouldn't believe.

Hermione and Ron Weasley are both Harry's friends,
Although they may argue they still make amends.
These characters feature in all of her books,
Amazing adventures with fearful spooks.

All of her books are a definite read,
When the sixth one arrives it's a must have need.
So sit back and wait with baited breath
And let's hope that it ends without Harry's death.

Ashley Griffiths (12)
Painsley Catholic High School

Great Minds Poem

It is really hard to choose a great mind in my life,
Think who has influenced me the most,
But there is one person who I think is a great mind,
I met him when I had to stay behind.
I met this special person,
He stood there with a smile
And something just clicked!
We met up more and more,
Our love grew and grew.
He influenced me to do what's right,
I just thought that maybe he might
Want to be with me forever
And here we are now!
He makes me laugh,
He makes me cry,
But one thing he wouldn't do is tell a lie.
When I am down he cheers me up,
I feel no hate,
All I can say is I love him so very much.
I love to hold him, kiss him, and feel him close to me.
He should be a famous great mind,
He really should,
So now I have expressed to you how I feel
About my special great mind.

Samantha Booth (15)
Painsley Catholic High School

Martin Luther King

Martin Luther King wanted to stop the madness,
After so long and what seemed to be an eternity of sadness.
He thought that all people were the same no matter what colour
or race,
But when he said anything white people laughed in his face.
He wanted no violence of any kind,
When the people heard they whined.
They wanted to hurt white people, as they had been hurt,
He then repeated no violence is needed, just drop your tools
and do no work.
Tucked up in bed Martin had a dream that black and white people
lived in peace,
And all the madness to finally cease.
Before he could realise his dream he was killed,
Shot in the back by a man so cunning, all dressed in black.

Jake Clarke (12)
Painsley Catholic High School

My Mother

Kind and caring,
Always sharing,
My mother is to me,
Just, maybe I could be
Like, my mother.
No! That's not at all me.

I look up to her,
Her face, it's soft like fur,
She is glamorous,
Yet she is friendly and kind,
Made up my mind,
Wish I was like my mother,
Oh well, never mind!

Katie Seaton
Painsley Catholic High School

Funky Friends

I have 4 friends,
They are called
Kathryn, Rachael, Annie and Grace,
They are the best.

Kathryn has brown hair,
Rachael has light brown hair,
Annie has blonde hair
And Grace has light brown hair.

All of my friends are 11,
They are going to be 12 soon.
Two of my friends,
Been together with me the longest.

They wanted to be friends with me,
It was really nice,
It is really special to me,
But our friendship will never end.

Thu Anh Nguyen (11)
Painsley Catholic High School

Great Minds

G andhi is a great mind because he
R eally helped the Indians to get their independence.
E very Indian owes their thanks to him.
A dolf Hitler is a fine example of power in the wrong hands,
T reating all those Jews so badly.

M other Theresa dedicated her life to homeless, sick people.
I saac Newton discovered the theory of gravity.
N ightingale was the founder of nursing as a profession.
D arwin was a scientist who developed the modern
   theory of evolution.
S hakespeare was a very famous English dramatist and poet.

Christopher Bevans (15)
Painsley Catholic High School

Let's Make The World A Better Place With Atomic Bombs

A great mind knows when to stop
And what's right and wrong.
A great mind has the wisdom to know
He doesn't know everything.

So, you up there, what would it be
Like to fall from your pedestal
And take your hand from the
Strings of the puppets you control?

He mocks me with his words,
'Let's make the world a better place'.
Why don't we hold peace talks,
Sat on atomic bombs?
And let's shake left hands
Because the right's holding a gun.

Let's blame Iraq,
Let's launch some bombs,
Let's smile and laugh for the folks back home
While the sky explodes.

Or maybe it's best that you're so blind
Because I know your heart can't grieve
What your eyes can't see.
No your heart can't grieve
What your eyes can't see.

You were my favourite part
Of our dead century.

Ross Daniels (15)
Painsley Catholic High School

Finally

How do you make friends?
Most of my brothers and sisters have friends,
I seem to be the odd one out.
I mean, I have tried just about everything I can,
I wish I had friends.

I could try again tomorrow but will I get the same result?
If I could make a friend I could start my life again,
But this time with someone to help me,
Someone to support me all the way,
That is how I would like to live my life.

The start of a new day,
Into the school gates, the teacher comes to me
And asks for me to look after a new child.
Yes, this is my chance,
Yes, I have made a friend, finally!

Ben Willis (13)
Painsley Catholic High School

Dizzy

Bart why are you so smart?
You're mental sometimes
And all you want is food, food, food all the time.
Say food or walkies
And you jump up and fetch your ball.
Say vet and you don't care.
Strangers go by and you bark all the time.

Mum's so dizzy,
She's always busy cleaning.
Loves gardening in the summer,
Always kind,
She's always there, rain or shine.

Christopher Toplass (11)
Painsley Catholic High School

Dan

My mate Dan,
My mate Dan is funny,
He is always kind and happy,
He is a good chappy.

His long fuzzy hair is like a squirrel's tail.
Dan is always kind and helpful,
Him and his smile,
What a lady charmer.

My mate Dan,
My mate Dan is protective,
Protective of his stuff,
If a woman smiled at him he would bluff.

He puts others first,
Making fresh friends each day.
A good, funky friend,
He has a smelly bottom end!

Declan Worrall (11)
Painsley Catholic High School

What I Put Up With!

My mum is very kind when she gives me sweets.
She's also tough when she plays fighting.
She also gets angry when I hit my brother.
When my mum goes out she always wears posh clothes.

My dad is very tall, 6' 4" he says but I think he's bigger.
He's also fun when he plays fighting with me.
My dad does the same as my mum when he gets angry.
My dad has two jobs, a teacher and a salesman at Esporta.

My brother is 7 years old but he acts like an 11 year old.
Sometimes when my brother gets bullied he asks for my help.
My brother is fun when we play fighting.
Sometimes my brother's silly when we play with swords.

Daniel Harrison (11)
Painsley Catholic High School

My Cool Family

My mum is kind,
She ain't nobody else's mum,
She's mine,
She takes me shopping,
She doesn't like stopping,
But she's my mum.

My dad is cool,
He doesn't like taking me to school,
It's embarrassing,
That's why I never ask him,
But he's my dad and he's cool.

My sister is annoying,
She's very bossy,
That's what's so annoying,
She can't help herself,
But to give a little shout,
She's my sister and she's annoying.

Jodie Carnwell (11)
Painsley Catholic High School

Pele

He ran down the pitch
Like it was a stitch.
He hopped over players
Like he was their slayers.

He used all his skill
And told the defenders to chill.
He ran past them all
And never did fall.

He shot at the keeper
Who was a real weeper.
You could never forget
The ball in the net.

Thomas Roughton (13)
Painsley Catholic High School

My Goldfish

I have a goldfish called Smoky and he has a tank to himself,
On his very own table, rather than a shelf.
I had an argument with my brother in the room where Smoky lives,
I wonder what Smoky would say if he could speak,
Whilst doing death-defying dives.
I wonder what Smoky would say once Christmas Eve had passed,
Would he tell me every little detail, very, very fast
Or would he rather not talk about it, for he might give away the past?

Would Smoky tell me every little detail of his life
Or would he tell me of every trouble and strife?
Would he like his nice clean tank
Or would he rather be on a big, dirty river bank?
Why is his facial expression so bleak?
Would he tell me if his tank has a leak?
But really, it is not a goldfish's place to speak.

Josh Leech (11)
Painsley Catholic High School

The Tiger

If it was a human it would have short, orange hair.
If it was a human it would have sharp teeth.
If it was a human it would be quite naughty.
If it was a human it would be nasty.
If it was a human it would be really fast.
If it was a human it would be quite strong.
If it was a human it would not be too bright.
If it was a human it would be very independent.
If it was a human it would be quite loud.
If it was a human it would be roughly clothed.
If a tiger was a human . . .

Jack Ward (11)
Painsley Catholic High School

The Bouncing Tiger

It waits in the tall green grass
Waiting for the right moment to *pounce!*
Its eyes watching and its teeth showing,
Its claws sharpened ready to *strike!*

Camouflaging itself behind trees and in the grass,
Approaching its prey in complete silence,
Making no sound at all.

Pouncing from out of the tree
With a mighty roar
And sinking its teeth into
The animal's flesh.

Slowly walking off to find a
Place to have a rest,
Ready for the evening hunt.

James Homer (12)
Painsley Catholic High School

My Dad

He helps me when I am down
By acting like a clown.
If I am in the wrong
He will always put me right.
If my work is incorrect
He will give me clues to how I must do it right.
If I am scared
He will be there,
He gives me advice
To help me face others.
He is always funny
But can be annoying too.
These are some of the reasons
My dad is my great mind.

Sophie Wye (14)
Painsley Catholic High School

Creatures Great And Small

Snakes are creatures that slither around,
Some slide up trees,
Others stay on the ground,
They have rough scales that are tough and strong,
They slither and slide, they are extremely long.

Tigers are creatures that growl a lot,
Some of them play,
While others hunt in day,
They eat zebra and deer,
Lots of other thing, that's a fear.

Crocodiles are creatures that snap,
Some get their own way,
Others are caught and far away,
They have a leather-type skin,
A bit like a shark, but without the fin.

Rachael Jackson (11)
Painsley Catholic High School

The Unique

My mum's organised, a great cook too,
Dad works hard and is helpful,
My brother is annoying but makes me laugh.

I like to play netball, gym and hockey,
I like to read at home,
I also like to shop or be with friends.

Two cats, two rabbits and tropical fish,
My cats like to cause trouble
But I love them all the same.

My mum, dad and brother,
Very unique I know,
That's how I like them, unique.

Sophie Mills (11)
Painsley Catholic High School

Super Mum!

My mum is the best,
You could never guess.
My mum is a great cook,
Unique, that's my mum,
Most people agree.

Intelligent is my mum,
She's so creative and smart.
To my bedroom, it is so sparkling clean (not).
Observing it carefully,
She will find it is not.

So there is my mum, so beautiful and clean,
She works so hard,
I could not have wished for a better mum.
She is so helpful and kind,
I love my mum.

Gemma Bailey (11)
Painsley Catholic High School

Important People

My friend is Georgina Miceli,
She's always watching the telly.
She's my friend
And our friendship shall never end.

How could I live without
The best person in the world,
His name is Tom
And he is always such a bomb.

Michelle has always been such a great pal,
Can't forget Jack he's the head of the pack.

What about Joe Rapercheter,
Can't forget him because
He's going to be the next Eminem rapper.

James Bailey (11)
Painsley Catholic High School

This Is What My Family Are

My mum is a bright, hard-working person who is super at things,
She sometimes moans but she is always an organised person.
My dad is sometimes forgettable but he is intelligent
At doing DIY because he does it most of the time.

My brother, a crying monster, makes you angry but he is
                                        sometimes good.
My older sister is a person who is stuck into schoolwork
And sometimes gets on your nerves.
Then again my younger sister is a menace who gets on your nerves
And never leaves you alone.

My family all make a noise sometimes,
I think my family are people who sometimes work hard
And sometimes do not work.
I also work hard sometimes too.

Joseph Rapacchietta (11)
Painsley Catholic High School

What I've Always Had To Put Up With!

My sisters keep annoying me,
Shouting and shouting.
My head keeps on spinning,
I don't know where I'm going.

I'm in a fantasy world,
I keep on running and running.
I try to escape
But I'm still there.

In a way I love my family,
No matter how much *noise* they make.
They're the best family
Anyone can wish for.

Siobhan Killeen (11)
Painsley Catholic High School

The Annoying Family

My family are great
But we always have a debate,
My mum is called Sharon and she is never in,
My dad is called Jason and he's the chef.

My brothers are annoying, just like a buzzing bee,
My big brother Kristian, he's 16, he's alright,
But when I am asleep
He wakes me up in the middle of the night.

My nan spoils me,
Sometimes she thinks I am a baby,
Or maybe . . .
A bunny.

My little brother Liam, he is very annoying,
He is into football,
My other brother Thomas, he's alright,
But he can be very loud
But altogether I love them.

Chelsey Baggley (11)
Painsley Catholic High School

Richard The Lion Heart

Slashing through the fields with a shining sword of light,
With his army behind him, charging with their might.
When the enemy saw him they were scared of his might.
There was only one person left and he was on a hill,
So everyone knew who to kill.

Samuel Freeman
Painsley Catholic High School

Angel Friend!

Carly is someone who is always there,
She is a friend who actually cares.

She may have a voice like a foghorn,
But she stands out like a rose between two thorns.

Her long, golden hair is like a caramel river,
Her character's so warm it won't make you shiver.

She has a slim figure,
You won't dare to snigger.

Her style is so great,
There's nothing about her I hate.

She runs around with a cheerful smile on her pretty face,
I suppose that's because she's playing kiss chase!

So there it is, the poem about her,
She's just like an angel wrapped up in fur.

Helen Wood (13)
Painsley Catholic High School

Beverley Rushton's Mind

My thoughts are like a lot of feathers put together,
I think about my friend when she is out of school.
I daydream about home time from school,
I wonder what I am going to have for tea.
I talk to myself about where my bus will be,
I think about which room do I go in next.
I daydream about chocolate, when I am hungry,
It's like Heaven.
I wonder where I am,
I talk to myself and say, *what time is it?*
I think about what I want to be when I grow up,
I wish I could fly over the world.
My thoughts are like a lot of feathers put together.

Beverley Rushton (11)
Painsley Catholic High School

My Special Friend Helen

Helen is her name,
Elizabeth is her middle name,
She stands out from the rest,
Like a damsel in distress.

Everybody calls her Helen the Melon,
As her name always rhymes with melon,
She has such a lively character,
As she laughs and jokes all day long.

Her hair, blonde, flowing in streaks,
Like a coat of camel's hair,
She has such a great figure,
You'd never want to snigger.

You would never want to hate her,
As she's so kind
And the best friend anyone could ever have.

Carly Plant (13)
Painsley Catholic High School

Safety Net

When you need help
They're sure to come

If you've won a cup
They'll share your glory

When you are lost
They'll show you the way

If you are in a hole
They will get you out

If you fall
They will catch you

Always there
Just to have fun with.

Lexie Hankinson (13)
Painsley Catholic High School

People Close To You

They are there for you,
To help you when you're down,
They will care for you,
And make you feel proud,
They will put a roof over your head,
Make sure you have a warm bed,
They will feed you,
Feed you till you're dead.

They will show you love and care,
They will be there for you,
There until you're dead,
They will never leave you,
Stay with you all the way,
They're your family,
They will never go away,
You can't change them,
They're yours to the last day.

Will Tatlow (13)
Painsley Catholic High School

Rock Until You Drop

Chillies, they are hot to eat
But they really can beat
Their drumming is good
It is so loud that I have to pull up my hood

They play great music all of the time
Unlike most bands they don't even mime
They rock all night long
And never miss off a song.

Liam O'Neill (13)
Painsley Catholic High School

What Makes A Mate

What is it to have a mate?
To have a mate
Is the best thing in the world.

Mates are loyal,
They're around when you're down,
They make you laugh.

When you're in need,
They help you through it,
No matter how hard or easy.

They keep your secrets,
Also your pride,
They will do anything for you,

That's what mates are!

Josh McVeigh (13)
Painsley Catholic High School

The Twin Towers

The Twin Towers stood up tall
Until they began to fall
The plane flew with so much power
It crashed straight into the towers

When it hit there was so much trouble
Because it was left in so much rubble
People stood there shouting and screaming
Now it stays with them when they are dreaming

It has stayed with people their whole life
Because they might have lost their wife.

Elliott Bateman (13)
Painsley Catholic High School

They're Here

Knock, knock, knock,
The squeaky door opened,
They're here, oh no!
The family has arrived.

Looking like royalty,
With their fancy hats
And their polished shoes,
They slowly walked towards me.

Shaking in my skin,
I managed to smile,
As fake as it was,
They smiled back.

Slowly they sat down,
Looking down their noses,
Scowling in disgust,
At the plainness of the room.

She got up,
The worst of them all,
Auntie Zelda,
The fashion designer.

Reaching for her bag,
Her long stick-thin fingers,
Brought out a sheet of paper,
She slammed it on the table.

She beckoned to the rest,
Up they got,
Her little slaves,
They all had gone.

Scared to death,
I picked up the paper,
Sweat running off my forehead,
I slowly looked down.

Nothing there,
No mark, nothing,
Was I going blind?
The sheet was blank.

Elizabeth Harper (13)
Painsley Catholic High School

Lonely

I walked down the road
The weather was cold
I felt scared of the world
As the cars scowled at me.

The wind hit me hard
I didn't want to fight
The shops were dead
The people had gone home.

I needed to see
Someone that knew me
I walked passed a gang
Their eyes burnt a hole through me.

I heard a voice
A voice I'd heard before
My eyes followed the sound
My heart filled with joy.

I was no longer lonely
I was no longer scared
I had the best company ever
My best friend in the world.

Lorna Horton (14)
Painsley Catholic High School

Kirsty's Mind

My thoughts are like a pile of books, they pile up in my mind.
They enter my mind like a racing car,
I think about my dad's friend taking his driver's test, will he pass?
I talk to myself about my homework, it's like a prison.
I wonder what I will have for tea, but I'll have to wait and see.
I daydream of my mum, she is the best.
I think about going home, I can't wait to have a rest.
These are some of my thoughts but I have a lot more . . .
I talk to myself about school, it can be a bit of a bore.
I think about my dog, as he is cute like a newborn baby.
I wonder about the world, will it end?
I daydream of my boyfriend, he is as fit as a runner.
I think about my life, it's really good like a new film.
My thoughts are like a pile of books, they pile up in my mind.

Kirsty Shaw (11)
Painsley Catholic High School

Henry VIII

Henry VIII was a mean old man,
With so many wives he didn't know when to stop,
If someone crossed him or made him mad,
He simply gave them the chop.

Henry VIII had three children,
Edward, Elizabeth and Mary,
Henry was fat and ugly,
And often came across as quite scary.

When Henry fought in battles he often lost,
Went down with no victory,
But because Henry was mean and nasty,
We all study him in history.

Jessica Roberts (12)
Painsley Catholic High School

Best Biker

My favourite sport is downhill biking
It is the only sport that I am liking
I like to do races
I always come in top places.

I win race after race
Cup after cup
My quick thinking and tactics
Would shut any opposition up.

When I come home from a victory
Them races are so easy
I hope to be the best one day
Just like my dad, Mr Maingay.

My dad is the best biker
He is now a millionaire
When he races so very fast
He gives me a bit of a scare.

Jake Ufton (12)
Painsley Catholic High School

Fizzog

My dad's big nose
Just grows and grows
Until it pokes me
In the ear

At the table
I'm not even able
To talk to my best friend's mate
Because my dad's big nose
Just grows and grows
Till it scoops all the food off my plate!

Adam McLeod (13)
Painsley Catholic High School

The Start

Setting out on the water
Boats in their thousands
Checking out the course for the very first time
The atmosphere is brilliant
Setting your countdown on the horn
Everybody gets ready
The start gets closer
5, 4 . . .
Everyone is sailing to the gate
3, 2 . . .
Bang! The gun sounds
Everybody is past the line
Sailing on the first beat
The boats are everywhere
The water once calm
Now white and wavy
The race has started
So has the clock.

Thomas Bland (12)
Painsley Catholic High School

Can You See?

They are there when you need them
They are there when you hate them
They help you when you are stuck
They help you when you are scared
They stay with you forever
They stay with you today
They will always be there for you
They will never leave you
You will now see
That they are family.

Christopher Ward (14)
Painsley Catholic High School

Sailing

My hobby is sailing
I think it's great
I love going fast
And jibing round corners
In the Laser Pico

I think tacking's boring
And very slow, compared
To running down in the wind
This is far more fun
Except when there's not a wind.

It's really boring waiting for a tow or a breath of wind
You sit there waiting and waiting
The main sheet flapping
In a more existing breeze
Then the orange safety boat comes round
'It's time to be off the water,' they say
'Come here, we'll give you a tow'
Then they rev the engine and shout
You reach the shore and that's the end.

Jonathan Wooldridge (12)
Painsley Catholic High School

Hey Mate!

F unny is what makes a friend
R edeeming himself if he's done something wrong
I like my friend, he's called Tyler Starkey
E veryone makes a mistake even if they are funny. He
N ever gives up
D on't interrupt, because he's my friend.

Nathan Alcock (13)
Painsley Catholic High School

In The Net

I like to play netball,
It's energetic and fun.
I play goal attack,
Shooting is my game.
Whoever we're against
I try to do my best.

Netball is fun
Because you can learn new steps.
Running with the ball, *tut, tut,*
It's not allowed.
Games don't last long,
But tire me out fast.

Now to round up what netball's about,
Being close as a team,
Learning with speed,
Keeping your eye on the ball,
You will never be sent to the wall.

Amy Plant (12)
Painsley Catholic High School

Chocolate

C hocolate tastes nice
H ow I wish for more
O range chocolate is my favourite
C reamy, crunchy, more
O h how I love chocolate
L ovely, melting, delicious chocolate
A s I eat more and more my
T ummy becomes fuller and fuller
E xquisite chocolate, all for me.

Catherine Deaville (11)
Painsley Catholic High School

Stanley Matthews

They called him Wizard of the Wing
One of the greatest players
He played for Stoke City and England.

Stanley Matthews was his name
A modest footballing hero
He helped Stoke become the best team of his time.

One of the greatest things he did
Was take his team right to the top
They won the Division One League Cup.

Perhaps Stoke City's greatest year,
They were riding top of the division
Just one game to go.

Stoke sold Stanley to Blackpool
They lost their game
And came second.

What a blow!
Who knows what would have happened
If Stanley Matthews was playing.

Alex Bamford (12)
Painsley Catholic High School

My Hobbies

M y hobbies are archery and drums
Y ou pull the string and shoot the arrow

H ave to have rhythm to play the drums
O r you can't play them at all
B oom on the bass drum
B ang on the toms
Y ou can play at concerts
S tages are good at gigs.

Nicky Roberts (12)
Painsley Catholic High School

Having Fun

Riding my bike,
A hobby I like,
Pushing the pedals around,
I cycle every night,
Up and down the hills I go,
Through the woods,
Over the fields.

Riding my bike,
A hobby I like,
People see me,
Stare and look at me,
Sometimes I think,
What is wrong?
Is it me or my bike?

Riding my bike,
A hobby I like,
As dangerous as it may be,
I ride with my friends,
All ten of them around,
I go up and down ramps,
And jump off walls.

Riding my bike,
A hobby I like,
I do it every day,
With all the gear,
Helmet, gloves and all,
Off I go, all ready and prepared,
For a night of fun.

Matthew Forrester (12)
Painsley Catholic High School

The Greatest

His name was Cassius Clay
No one knew what he could do in the ring
Boy were they shocked when they saw him
He was the greatest fighter around

He punched as hard as iron
His fists were as fast as flashing lightning
He moved like a ballerina
His opponents looked like amateurs

He won the heavyweight title
His amazing career took a wrong turn
His title was taken away
Because he wouldn't go to war

He was a Muslim, he refused
It was against all his beliefs
He was put in prison for this
He changed his name to Muhammad Ali

He came and won the title
Although he would not stop his training
He got really tired from his work
He was forced to retire with illness

Boxing gave him Parkinson's
Or so some said it did, but were they right?
Nevertheless he was the best
He is boxing's icon, a legend!

Joe Marlow (14)
Painsley Catholic High School

Big Belly

My dad has a really big belly,
He walks around and in front of the tele,
It looks like he's nine months pregnant.

My dad would not hurt a fly,
And he definitely would not lie,
But he drinks lots of beer.

People see him as a huge giant,
But I do not see that at all,
I say the bigger the better.

Many people think he's scary,
But I love him lots more,
He's my huge loveable hero.

I would do anything for him,
And he would do anything for me,
But I still say he's nine months pregnant.

Katy Buttress (13)
Painsley Catholic High School

Living My Life

M y dog can sit, roll over and lie down,
Y o dog, come here.

D o your tricks here,
O h no, not that one, sit, not lie down,
G ood boy, here have a treat.

C lever boy, you can do it,
H ere boy, have a go at this trick,
A nd have a bone,
R ight good boy,
L ovely, have another go,
I have a special treat for you,
E ffective, that looks excellent.

Jamie Capper (12)
Painsley Catholic High School

Blackadder Of Britain

E dmund Blackadder, an all-time British hero,
D ark and witty, certainly not a zero.
M alicious and scheming, always at his best,
U ndoubtedly far above the rest.
N ot very good at taking a drink,
D ives at the pint glass, without having to think.

B aldrick his dogsbody, not very smart at all,
L ittle and scrawny, his walk is more a crawl.
A nd Melchid, a fool in our majesty's court,
C harges into danger, without a second thought.
K ing of England, cares not for his two sons,
A lways at war, sounding the war drums,
D arling, a captain, who wants Edmund dead,
D esperate for the day in which he will have his head.
E ddy Blackadder, an all-time British zero,
R eally not the material to be called a hero.

Alexander Humphreys (15)
Painsley Catholic High School

A Friend Who You Cherish!

A friend can be the best thing in the world,
They are there to support you, no matter where you are.
They will help you when you are unhappy and distressed,
They can say something and make you feel important, special
                                    and on top of the rest.

They will smile and lighten up your day,
When you've just found out your faithful dog has died.
All they have to do is open their arms,
It is so meaningful and supportive, it can relight your heart.

They clear a path when you are blindfolded in the dark,
They supply the tissues when you are down in the dumps.
You don't have to move for them to know,
That is all it takes for a friend who you cherish.

Philippa Whitmarsh (13)
Painsley Catholic High School

Poetry

To write a poem is a difficult task,
A challenge to accomplish is what has been asked.
Should it include prose or maybe the odd rhyme,
Or should it contain verses all keeping in time?
But what would be the subject to bear in mind
When writing a poem line after line?
Must it consists of haikus, different from the rest
Or stick with rhyming couplets the way in which people know best?
What must it be based on, politics, science or war
Or maybe a taste of Shakespeare, Einstein them all?
Should it be inspired by a great role model, like Martin Luther King
Or include facts about life, to aid you in learning?
This task that has been set may be difficult and consuming,
But it all pieces together, like a puzzle, I'm assuming.
How long should a poem be, ten lines, maybe a page
Or does it depend on your ability or maybe your age?
All these questions that occur, connect to poetry,
Can be simply answered without you even knowing it.
Firstly, I say that it comes from the poet,
Whatever they're thinking that's all there is to it.
If their style if rhyming, verses or prose,
It all counts as poetry, anything goes.
The basis of your poem could be the things you most enjoy,
Or maybe personal experiences you would like to employ.
There is no right or no wrongs where poetry is concerned,
It is a time to show off your abilities learned.
There are no limitations to restrict your imagination,
Just uses your mind to create the perfect animation.
A poem could simply be a few words from your heart,
Or an essay explaining the wonders of art.
It's not such a challenge a task or a test,
Just an opportunity to show your thoughts at their best.
As witnessed right here, writing poetry is easy
You can write it about anything and stay trouble-free.
You don't need to stay pondering over two words,
Incorporate them both into poetry if that is preferred.
It shouldn't be complicated or hard to explain,
But thoughtful and interesting with no line the same.

Treat poetry as special, as precious as jewels,
Oh and when writing a poem, remember, no rules.
Don't worry about rhymes or making it first class,
Just write what you feel and I'm sure it will pass.
The one thing to remember is it is a pleasure and not pain,
And if you stick to these rules I'm sure you'll be writing poetry again.

Hannah Richardson (15)
Painsley Catholic High School

Don't Splash Your Cash

Shoppers of Britain,
Have you noticed that prices are high,
For almost everything we buy,
All this silly spending must now stop.

Our clothes are our gods,
And we splash our cash to buy some more,
No matter how tall or small,
Slowly all our cash will disappear in a flash.

If we do not stop spending soon,
We quickly will have nothing left,
There will be no terrific TVs except
In the tiny, compact shop windows.

The things we buy are overpriced,
The cost is like a sleepless night,
Or like the feeling of an unhappy flight,
Or as a new, red, broken kite.

So don't let your money run away from you,
Keep it in something sealed like a safe,
Don't leave it to fly away,
And spend it wisely, like I say.

David Hancock (13)
Painsley Catholic High School

Chum

My awesome mate
Tyler Starkey my bud
He is cool and is good
I like him because
He's like me
We know each other
From limb to limb.

He likes PlayStation
So do I
He likes cards
So do I
He likes cinema
So do I
There is one little difference
His hair is not like mine.

The one thing that links us together
Is that we have the same games on PlayStation 2
So we compare our fights
And whether we are good
This is why we're not weird
Unlike Ben our other friend.

I would say Tyler Starkey
Is like a clone of me
He stands out like a sore thumb
He is an individual
For being funny and dumb.

Cian Carroll (14)
Painsley Catholic High School

The Room

Door to my apartment is heavily locked
Can't answer the door even if knocked
I'm alone in my room
Am I going to live in endless gloom?
Hey, what's that noise in the bathroom?
There's a hole, does it end my doom?

As I ponder, why I can't get out
I think to myself no time to wander about
TV don't work, neither does the phone
Will I ever get out of my home?
As the night grows darker
I drop my permanent marker.

My heart stops
As my ears begin to pop
A sound from the hole sounded like a child
A voice so desperate and mild
I climb in the hole to find what's up
But now wondering if my time's up.

It's a nightmare, it is, I need my friend
But no one is there, my suffering will not end
It's a dream, a nightmare
Nothing in the world has made me this scared.

Tyler Starkey (13)
Painsley Catholic High School

Another Wasted Mind

The old man lived alone in a run-down apartment on a council estate.
Paper peeled from the walls, dust gathered on the shelves and
cobwebs hung in every corner.
No one came to visit, all his friends had long since departed.
He lived isolated from the outside world, save his weekly trip to the
local shop.
Occasionally, small boys would slowly creep up to knock on his door,
before hurriedly running away.
He would watch them leave and think back to his own childhood,
Back to when he was young and willing to learn . . .

He'd always known he was clever.
From an early age he could understand things, that his friends just
couldn't seem to grasp.
Slowly, he drifted apart from them and retreated into his own
solitary world.
He never went to school, with five brothers and sisters and his father ill
in bed, he was forced to stay home and act as the man of the house.
On many a day he would sit and stare out of the window, as the other
children went off to school.
His only comfort was inside his own head . . .

Inside his mind he saw castles and dragons,
He saw mountains and oceans,
He saw creatures no one else could imagine.
Inside his mind was a whole new world waiting to be discovered.
Strange to think that that young boy, with so much potential, so many
ambitions, was now 87 and living in a run-down apartment on a
council estate.
But that's just the way of the world . . .
Another wasted childhood,
Another wasted dream,
Another wasted mind.

Lorna Poole (16)
Painsley Catholic High School

Grosse Gemüter

There was this bloke I used to know,
Awfully old and awfully slow.
Wore a flat cap and walked with a stick,
Smoked sixty a day, and drank 'til he was sick.

He had a strange accent, Belgian or Polish,
Seemed half-and-half, just not quite wholish.
When I asked him about it, he'd look 'round and shout,
'Out of my vay, you horrible lout!'

Three inch-thick glasses over his eyes,
I thought him plain barmy, Mum thought him as wise.
'He fought in the war!' to his defence she would say.
'If he didn't then you'd speak in German today!'

A poor tortured soul, feeble and frail,
We tried to avoid him, lest he tell us a tale
Of Gerry, the Führer, blitzing and killing,
Stories he seemed to find strangely fulfilling.

He invited me in once, *yes!* (I might find
A new insight into this sharp-witted mind).
He took off his loafers and showed me his medal,
Then went into the kitchen to heat up the kettle.

I looked 'round the room, stuff from the war,
Littered the sofas, tables and floor.
Then I realised, all his friends died,
This smelly old man had a truly great mind.

But wait this token of bravery from the Second World War,
Where, where, oh where had I seen it before?
Then I remembered, 'twas pinned to the chest
Of a . . . German? Was his name . . . Rudolf Hess?

Yes! Of course! He was aide to the boss
Which would make this medal - the old Iron Cross!

Philip Milward (16)
Painsley Catholic High School

Extra Heads

Everyone needs friends,
They are always there,
Through thick and thin,
Good and bad,
Always there to help.

People that you care about,
Also that make you laugh,
Buy you presents,
Take you places,
Always have great fun.

Never let you down,
Always by your side,
Respect you,
Never give up on you,
Or leave you on your own.

Pay you compliments,
Bring you laughter,
Make you feel happy,
And feel good inside,
Friends are the best!

Leona Mould (13)
Painsley Catholic High School

My Mind

My mind is like a maze,
all busy and in a craze.

Thoughts enter my mind like a fast racing car,
My senses surround me telling me things near and far.

Memories come and go,
Future thoughts, I do not know.

My mind is like a maze,
all busy and in a craze.

Trevor Oliver (11)
Painsley Catholic High School

Stephen King

Stephen King has a great mind
He inspires me with ideas all of the time
The hairs on your neck are bound to rise
This is the type of book most people despise

I love his books, the titles vary
Stephen's books are ever so scary
Bags of bones, skeleton crew
Firestarter and the dead zone too

His books have a twist, it can be a real nightmare
I advise don't pick it up if you are easily scared
Tales to chill and freeze the blood
The spine-tingling terror to scare you good

His books are the best
They are far better than the rest
I wish Stephen would write more
Different titles I could adore.

Ashley Rommelrath (14)
Painsley Catholic High School

Colours

Purple, blue, green and red,
Colours everywhere in my head.
Sunshine is yellow, clouds are white,
Sparkly stars shine in the night.

They make me happy, make me smile,
Looking at a rainbow is quite worthwhile.
Orange, yellow, indigo, pink,
I often stop just to think of . . .
Red, orange, yellow, green, purple and blue.

Charlotte Bee (12)
Painsley Catholic High School

Greatest Minds Of Formula 1

M aclaren had Hakkinen
E very bit of track he would use.
R acing Schumacher was his game
C atching him he liked
E dging out to pass him
D arting down the inside
E asing on the brakes
S afely he makes the pass

B ennaton had Schumacher
E ddie Irvine joined him soon
N ick Hiedfeild is a newcomer, and
Z onta is too

M aclarens are the best
A yrton Senna drove for them
C ars couldn't get anywhere near them
L eaving them from the start
A yrton Senna was the best
R ewards of four World Championships
E ven now he is remembered, even though
N ow he's dead.

Jonathan Salt (14)
Painsley Catholic High School

My Mind

My thoughts are like lightning,
Thoughts enter my mind like switching on a TV.
I think about my life,
I think about computer games,
I dream about them every night.
I wonder how many games I've got,
I think about games like I think about my life.

Kieren Yates (11)
Painsley Catholic High School

Red Hot Chili Peppers

Red Hot, Red Hot, as they stand proud
The crowd worshipping the heroes' greatness
The song is immense
And the tune is extravagant
The beat is electrifying
Causing us to scream
Sound levels meet the maximum
Heart rates top the scales
And people begin to drown in the waves of sound
The song reaches a peak
Then the level begins to drop
And the beat begins to stop
The song has hit the end
But the memories still go on
As the crowd begin to leave
The guitars are put down
And a flicker of light catches the strings
And peace begins to enter.

James Beattie (14)
Painsley Catholic High School

My Mum

My mum is helpful
and very proud
she's so amazing.
She stands out in the crowd.

She helps families
and children that are bad.
She helps them build their lives together
it makes me quite sad.

She gives the parents respite
and the children a fun day out.
Everybody loves her,
it makes me quite proud.

Sally Mountford (12)
Painsley Catholic High School

My Balloon

My mind is like a flat balloon
deflating every second of my life.
My thoughts enter my balloon,
like a tortoise trying to walk a mile.
I think that my PlayStation 2 is like a big, exciting adventure.
waiting to be finished.
I think my parents are like two busy bees
always doing something to improve our family and our lives.
I think homework is like God
enslaving me and forcing me to do my homework.
Food is like an angel coming down to me giving me healing food
from Heaven.
Television makes me feel like
I'm bathing in a bubbly Jacuzzi.
My mind is like a flat balloon
deflating every second of my life.

Adam Newport (12)
Painsley Catholic High School

My Princess Diana Poem

Princess Diana was very kind,
She always had great thoughts on her mind.
The things she did were always helpful,
And she was everyone's guardian angel.

She was bold, intelligent and caring,
And also very amazing.
She visited people all over the world,
Looked after and gave them her word.

What she did was very courageous,
So she must have been conscientious.
Everyone is proud of her,
And people strongly miss her.

Abbi-Gayle Lindop (12)
Painsley Catholic High School

My Family

My dad's name is Russ,
He could lift a bus.
He's quite bright,
But still manages to bodge the lights,
But even so he's never a zero,
And will always remain my hero!

My mum's Linda,
She loves looking out the window.
She's always good fun,
She likes lying in the sun.
She's my number ten,
And my little mother hen.

Joe, he's my brother,
I wouldn't swap him for any other.
He likes to ride on his bike,
And loves singing, on my mic!
He's a mixture of Mum and Dad,
And he's the best thing I've ever had.

Nikki Lamonby (12)
Painsley Catholic High School

My Mind

I think about my mum and brother,
It is a nice thought.
I wonder about the world tomorrow.
Sleep is like a battery, charging me up at night.
I wonder what it is like at the bottom of the sea.
I wonder what it is like in space.
I wonder what it is like on top of Mount Everest.

Tom Goodwin (11)
Painsley Catholic High School

Laura's Poem

My mind is like a goldfish
because I always forget different things.
Thoughts enter my mind
like a rush of lightning.
I think about my mum and dad
because they are like a big block of chocolate
ready to be loved.
My thoughts turn to homework
which is like a big, black, stormy cloud,
ready to burst.
I wonder about food
because it is lovely.
My mind drifts to how I look
because it's like walking through Hell and back.
Thoughts spring into my head about my friends
who are like a big, fluffy pillow
ready to be jumped on.
My mind is like a goldfish
because I always forget different things.

Laura Pemberton (12)
Painsley Catholic High School

All Alone

Sitting in a small, dark room,
everything quiet and peaceful.
A small ray of light shimmering through
a small crack in the curtain.
Not a sound, complete silence,
all alone I seem to be,
and alone I will stay,
till my days are up and I'm no longer alive.
I will be alone,
       All alone!

Lisa Cotton (15)
Painsley Catholic High School

Christopher's Mind

My thoughts are like a big, white fog
Thoughts enter my mind as fast as a bolt of lightning.
I think about when school finishes; it is like Heaven.
I dream about seeing my dad and him giving me back my stuff,
it is a cloud of joy.
I wonder if my dad will ever give me back my stuff,
it's like a stream of sparkling water.
I wish to have my dog back, it's like wonder world.
I think about how much homework I have to do.
I have nightmares that I get killed and the planet blows up.
It's like a TNT.
I think of what will happen at the end of time.
I think it's like a smoke grenade.
I wonder what it will be like when I'm older like an old turtle.
I think about what it would be like with robots.

Christopher Allsop (11)
Painsley Catholic High School

Great Minds

She's always been there to love and protect,
She's the one I look up to, admire and respect.
She gives me encouragement and praises my strengths,
I hope I live up to what she expects.

She helps me out when I struggle and strive,
She's the greatest influence I've got in my life,
She gives me advice and a shoulder to cry on,
In life I'll be lost if ever she's gone.

She is my mum and my best friend,
I hope she'll be there till the end,
Taken for granted, but I can see,
My mum will always be there for me.

Sarah Rushton (15)
Painsley Catholic High School

Siobhan's Mind

My thoughts are like a fast car
carrying lots of wonders into my mind.
Thoughts enter my mind like the whispering wind,
so it's not hard to find.
I think about things, homework, maths and dinner.
I wonder if I could have a car,
go places that I've never seen.
My thoughts are like a fast car,
carrying lots of wonders into my mind.
Thoughts enter my mind like a misty fog
just waiting to be seen.
I daydream about my work at school,
could I make it better?
I sometimes talk to myself about a question.
'Is this right?
Is it wrong?
What is the answer?'
My thoughts are like a fast car
carrying lots of wonders into my mind.
Will they be seen?

Siobhan Wallace (12)
Painsley Catholic High School

Nelson Mandela

He stood for what he thought was right
And then he paid the price.
For many years they locked him up,
A big part of his life.

He shouldn't have been punished
For wanting equal rights
He gave his message loud and clear,
The same for black and white.

Natalie Wolff
Painsley Catholic High School

The Premiership

T aking corners and free kicks,
H alf-time calling, 2-1 down,
E nergetic, exciting, that's the Premiership.

P uffing and panting, not long to go,
R uud and Rooney, Ronaldo and Reyes,
E xhausted defenders, exhausted defending,
M aking goalkeepers force that final save.
I n tune fans chanting, 'We will rock you!'
E xpectant managers with millions to spend,
R eferee blows his half-time whistle,
S weaty men and sweatier shirts,
H appy players score the match-winning penalty,
I njecting life into that lifeless ball,
P erfect blend for a perfect game!

Christopher Millward (15)
Painsley Catholic High School

The Scientist

The scientist sits over the microscope,
His thick-rimmed glasses falling off the end of his nose,
Three hours later, he turns off the lights,
And looks into a large dark lab,
He remembers when he was young,
The bullying he was a victim of,
He remembers the punch, the kick,
Studied long and hard to get away from the pain,
Nobel Peace Prize coming his way?
His fantastic brain, filled with knowledge,
Just shows a brilliant mind,
Is not always an appreciated one.

Rosalyn Greatbatch (15)
Painsley Catholic High School

Shell-Shocked

I am all alone
Surrounded by people
Always on my own.

My friends, they leave me
Don't need me, I'm useless
But one day they'll see.

Someday they'll find
That they do need me,
I am important,
They'll be shell-shocked, you'll see.

Left by myself to
Recover from my life,
They don't have a clue.

They all hate me
But pretend that nothing's wrong,
One day they'll see.

Someday they'll find
That they do need me,
I am important,
They'll be shell-shocked, you'll see.

Pretend they like me,
I told you they would,
They all move me really.

They try to tell me
It's all been in my head,
I don't believe them.

Someday they'll find
That they do need me,
I am important,
They'll be shell-shocked, you'll see.

Elisa Etemad (15)
Painsley Catholic High School

Entering My Mind

My mind is like a zoo,
It's wild.

Thoughts jump into my head like Tigger.

One thought is homework,
It's like a black cloud covering the sun.

The second thought is going home,
It's like a ray of sunshine shining through the dark cloud.

The third thought is when I wonder what I'm going to watch on TV,
It's as funny as Homer Simpson.

The fourth thought is watching my nan when she's drunk,
It's as funny as watching her fall over.

The fifth thought is being grounded,
It's as bad as watching Neighbours.

James Morgan (12)
Painsley Catholic High School

Fame

Living the life of the rich and famous,
How easy must it be?
Fast cars, money, glamour,
It's definitely for me!
Awards, parties and premiers,
Eventually becoming millionaires!
But would life really be that good?
Constantly being judged,
Paparazzi everywhere,
Your private life always shared.
All the expectations of your fans,
Fame really is not in your own hands.

Jennifer Keeling (15)
Painsley Catholic High School

Staring Creativity

A man stares at a blank canvas,
Where others see nothing, he sees a painting,
A painting of sunset against roaring waves.
Another man stares at a guitar,
Where others see a guitar, he sees a band,
A band that is successful and well-known.
A woman stares at a sculpture, she sees its influence,
The influence of the artist's emotion, blood, sweat and tears,
A group stares at the ocean,
Where others see water, they see a playground,
A playground of depths, exploration, and a holder of secrets.
A scientist stares at a formula,
Where others just see symbols, he sees a meaning,
The meaning of new discoveries and greater possibilities.
A teacher sees his students,
Where others just see children, he sees people,
A lawyer, a policeman, a doctor or two and other occupations.
I see a person in the mirror,
Where others just see the outside, I see the inside.
The most important thing in life
Is a person's
Own style,
Own creativity,
And a heart to match.

Andrew Cope (15)
Painsley Catholic High School

Nasty Past

On a cold winter's night
Jack the Ripper sets off from his house.
His frost bitten windows gleaming under the twinkling moon.
As the Ripper sets off down Alan Drive he sees his next victim
A young boy about the age of twenty.
He was wearing blue jeans and a black jumper
He staggered up to his victim and commits a vile deed
He has struck again!
Will he ever stop?
Three weeks later he becomes Britain's most wanted man
The search over London is on and all the Peelers set off
Looking for the most dangerous man in Britain.
He was finally found a few months later
He was hung in Newgate Prison.
He has finally been stopped.

David Fisher (11)
Painsley Catholic High School

Questioning The Great Minds

What is a great mind?
Louis Pasteur, Marie Curie, Albert Einstein?
The scientist, the philosopher, the architect, the doctor . . . ?

But who are the real great minds, closer to home?
Perhaps the writer, who sits all alone in the study,
Writing novels, stories, poems and thesis . . .

And what is intelligence?
Is it the ability to quote facts from a text book,
Like some relentless - perpetual machine?

No! We all have great minds. We are intelligent.
Just in different ways . . .

Jenette Graham (15)
Painsley Catholic High School

Two Sides To Love

When you find love, you know it's for real,
It's the only emotion you can truly feel.
When you feel cared for, you go funny inside,
The thoughts of love you can't seem to hide.
Love is magical and a feeling of ease,
You'll do anything to try to please,
The one you love, the love that's for real.
Love can go wrong, hearts can break,
A flow of emotions, of anger and hate.
Through times of anger, no matter how strong,
The love is still in your heart and will be for so long.
Through break-ups and fights, the love you'll deny,
In your mind you'll never forget what they mean to your life,
Your first ever love and love of all time.

Joanne Healey (15)
Painsley Catholic High School

My Fat Cat

I have a fat tabby cat,
He loves to sleep on the mat,
He eats lots of food,
Which puts him in a good mood,
Then plods along,
To look in the pond,
To find a fish or two.
He licks his lips
And has fish and chips.
He goes through the door
And falls flat on the floor,
After a hard day's work.

Michael Tyers (13)
Painsley Catholic High School

Ryan's Mind

My thoughts are like a cheetah, one minute there and then gone.
I think about a cheetah, it is the fastest animal in the world.
I daydream about myself being late for something.
I wonder what time it is.
I talk to myself if I am stuck sometimes.
I think about everything, but most of all a cheetah.
My thoughts are like a cheetah, one minute there and then gone.
I think about what is going to happen.
I think that I am going to have a good day.
I feel like a cheetah when I sprint past my friends.
No matter how fast I run they don't seem to catch me.
When I'm tired I go to sleep, just like a cheetah, tired from running.
Cheetah one minute there then gone.

Ryan Hurst (12)
Painsley Catholic High School

Leaves

Leaves falling slowly down and down,
Time seems to stop until they reach the ground,
All shapes, tones, colours and size, they spring alive
In autumn but go to sleep in lines.
Row by row, line by line they stand still until
That time comes near when a gentle breeze comes blowing here,
Instantly they shudder with cold; how could the wind be so bold,
As to disturb their slumber with such power,
As to wake them for that hour,
'How rude!' they scream in crackled tones,
'For you to wake us in our homes!
'All we wish to do is sleep
So how do we deserve this intrusion?'

David Goodwin (13)
Painsley Catholic High School

My Thoughts

My mind is like a light bulb;
it turns on and off,
but it can blow up.

Thoughts enter my mind
like a Ferrari; fast.

I think about my PlayStation 2,
it's like chocolate, very addictive.

My thoughts turn onto homework,
it's like maths; boring.

I wonder about Christmas,
it's like winning the lottery.

My mind drifts to my grandma,
she is like flowers; nice and smelly.

Thoughts spring into my mind about TV,
it's like the Queen,
sometimes boring, sometimes good.

My mind is like a light bulb,
it turns on and off,
but it can blow up.

Tom Sims (12)
Painsley Catholic High School

The Football Trials

Me and some mates went for the footie trials
But then the coach made us run for miles!
Then he put us in a match, eleven a side,
When the players saw their opponents they tried to hide!
At the end our coach said, 'Well done, I'm quite impressed!'
And all the boys cheered, 'Yeah, we're the best!'

Liam Mountford (11)
Painsley Catholic High School

Joe's Mind

My thoughts are like a sock drawer,
Thoughts enter my mind like greased lightning,
I think about work,
it's like Hell.
I daydream about creating my own computer,
I will be rich.
I dream about having a lie-in,
it will never happen.
I talk about going home early,
it's further and further away in my mind.
I think about eating a lot more than I should -
but it will make me fat.
I dream about no homework,
it never comes true.
I dream about sleep,
it always comes true.
I talk to myself about no school in the winter,
if only it would come true.
I think about not being ill
so I could see my friends.
I daydream about good luck,
so I will not be ill anymore.
My thoughts are like a sock drawer.

Joseph Swanston (11)
Painsley Catholic High School

The Waves

The sea is a terrible monster
So fierce that if anyone went in there
They were going to get washed away.
It hit the mountain walls
And blocked it off like a bulldozer smashing things
Like it was on a construction site
The worst one is coming, a tidal wave
It's smashing boats like a boa constrictor.

William Campbell (12)
Painsley Catholic High School

Was It Worth It?

'I have a dream'
The magical words from Martin L King
All the things he would have seen,
Throughout his extraordinary life.

All of the protests,
All of the stands,
All of the speeches,
Was it worth it?

Fighting for racial rights,
Followed by thousands and thousands,
Black was his race,
He was determined to fight for it.

All of the protests,
All of the stands,
All of the speeches,
Was it worth it?

M was for manpower
L was for love
K was for his kind heart
Martin Luther King!

All of the protests,
All of the stands,
All of the speeches,
Was it worth it?

James Wood (15)
Painsley Catholic High School

Olivia's Mind

My mind is like a jumbled up puzzle
Thoughts come into my mind so fast and so often just like a cheetah.
Then they go out like a flick of a switch and never come back.
The thoughts I sometimes get are about things that I want in the future
Or something I want for Christmas.
Most of the time I daydream
And it just gives me time to think things through and sort my head out.
My thoughts are like one thousand dreams that have come true
All at once because I feel that I have understood my work
And gained a benefit from the knowledge and experience
Passed on to me by my parents and teachers.
Other times I wish that they would go away
Because they keep on bugging me
As if there was two devils sitting on my shoulders
Pulling me in both directions and telling me different things to do.
My mind looks into other people's minds
And I try to anticipate the feelings of the other person
And what they are thinking inside,
It is like I can mind read, it feels so strange.
My mind can sort things out and figure out things
That I desperately want to know,
Things that I need to know for the future
And things I have learned from the past,
This also helps to keep me safe from harm
As these instincts protect me from dangers.
When I look into someone's face, all I can see if the person's mind
Working away the same was as mine, I think.
Sometimes I feel like shouting out loud
Because of some of the thoughts I have had that day
As I feel that sometimes I have not been fully understood,
Which can be very frustrating.
But I can say that on the whole my mind is a busy mind
And a happy one too!

Olivia Healy (11)
Painsley Catholic High School

Jiggerly, My Pet Giraffe

Big brown spots like chocolate drops
As tall as a willow tree
His tail moves to and fro
His feet move swift and silently
As through the grass he goes.

His face is long and slender
Eyes framed with lashes, curled, long and dark
His glance is soft and tender
And a tongue rough as tree bark.

He stops close, quite near to me
And drops his heavy head upon my arm
I feel his breath, it's moist and warm
His nose, shiny and black like polished boots.

I reach up and stroke his brow
And whisper,
'Jiggerly, my favourite friend
You're free to roam this plain, it's safe from trophy hunters
Come and visit me again.'

Samantha Bloor (11)
Painsley Catholic High School

Rowling Mad

J K Rowling is the best,
She writes stories better than the rest.
Her books are amazing, I can't put them down,
If they were water I would drown.
She has now become a millionaire,
From selling her books everywhere.
You can buy her books in W H Smiths
And give them to people as great gifts.
She writes about Ron, Hermione and Harry Potter,
Harry is great and there's no one hotter.

Alex Oakden (13)
Painsley Catholic High School

My Best Friend . . . My Dog Patch

P erfectly postured he catches his ball in the breeze,
   landing softly, standing proud.
A s he splashes in the river, he makes us laugh and chuckle,
   splashes us with mud and water in the middle of the summer.
T apping his feet across the wooden floor, he sits next to my dad
   and begs for his supper with his drooping eyes and wet, splodgy
   nose, we give him meat and gravy to last him till the morn.
C rashing thunder, he whimpers away, hiding in tiny corners,
   'Don't go in the bedroom,' my mum yells at him,
   not knowing what to do I comfort him.
H olidays we go on, we wave goodbye to him, sitting there all alone
   crying as we drive away. When we come to pick him up, he jumps
   up with delight, this is how we know he's missed us
   after all those nights.

Lisa Dawson (11)
Painsley Catholic High School

Siobhan's Mind

My thoughts are like lightning
Thoughts enter my mind like a cheetah.
I think about my mum she is like the next Jamie Oliver.
I daydream about chocolate it's like Heaven in a box.
I wonder about the world, it's like a hotel because lots
                           of people stay there.
I talk to myself about the weather,
It's like a whale it is unpredictable.
I think about shopping and how it's like my best dream come true.
I think about lightning it is like the blink of an eye.
I wonder about the sea and oceans - like a whole new world.
I daydream about my dad he's the cuddliest toy on the planet.

Siobhan Williams (11)
Painsley Catholic High School

Jacob Collier's Mind

My thoughts are like a milk float moving slowly in my mind.
My thoughts enter my mind like one big race.
I think about my tea, will it taste delicious?
I daydream about who will be at school, and what they will be doing.
Sometimes I wonder what it would be like, missing the bus.
At times I picture what I could do when I get home.
Some days I think, *will I get told off today?*
When a football match is on, I wonder what the score will be.
There are times when I think, *what are my family doing?*
I sometimes wonder if I could have changed things, but still have a grey day.
Sometimes I wonder what I will learn today and forget like an elephant.
On days when I am racing I will run like the wind.
My thoughts are like a milk float, moving slowly in my mind.

Jacob Collier (11)
Painsley Catholic High School

My Friends Poem

M y friends are great. Here they come
'Y o,' they say.

F rom the long black gate
R obbie's tall and likes to talk, Finny's small and loves his sport.
 I ncoming! Whacky Sam, making a jerk of himself.
E very day Matthew asks for cheats
N o, I say, not today.
D own the stairs the end of the day, all the girls standing in my way.
S ee my friend at next play, going home that's made my day.

Oliver McLeod (11)
Painsley Catholic High School

Weather

It swirls and sways
It changes each day
It sprinkles and pours
Rain on the floor,
It snows and snows
Snowmen get built,
It shines and shines
Children feel fine,
Beautiful rainbows come out
When it rains and shines,
It sways and glides,
Leaves fall off the trees,
Hair blowing in the wind,
We don't know what it's like at night
Because everyone is sleeping tight.

Kirsty Brassington (11)
Painsley Catholic High School

Emma's Mind

My thoughts are like dreams as they enter my head
as fast as a racing car,
I think about work, it is like building a wall,
I dream about dolphins as they splash me with joy,
I wonder one day if I could have a cat as it plays with a ball of wool,
I talk to myself about handwriting club as I wrinkle myself up,
I think about my family as they pray for me,
My thoughts are like dreams as they enter my head
as fast as a racing car.

Emma Gotham (11)
Painsley Catholic High School

Matthew's Mind

Homework is like a chain, keeping me at home.
Daydreaming about home is like actually being there.
I feel hungry as a pig when I'm thinking about my tea.
I often think, *will I finish my homework or go on for ever?*
I wonder if my cat is at home or wandering away.
Will the weather tomorrow be dry or wet?
I daydream about getting in bed on time or being late.
What lessons will I have tomorrow or will I be ill?
I hope my weekend is fun and not boring.

Matthew Cooper (11)
Painsley Catholic High School

Netball

N etball - nice, I've played for a while.
E veryone playing netball makes me smile.
T rying my hardest to score a goal,
B all in my hands
A ll players look
L onging for us to win
L iving for netball.

Helena Knight (12)
Painsley Catholic High School

Netball

N etball
E nergy-filled
T eams A and B
B est game there is
A club I play for
L ively and energetic
L ife without netball, I can't imagine.

Charlotte Wright (11)
Painsley Catholic High School

C S Lewis

The enthralling, electrifying mind of C S Lewis,
Wrote the mesmerising, intoxicating books of Narnia.

Pick up one of the witty series
You will think no more of your agonies.

You will be enraptured, encaptured, exported, transported,
To a colossal world with Aslan and the witch.

It is magical, mystical, fabulous, ingenious,
It takes you on a journey you will never forget.

Neglect your worries, neglect your frets,
Indulge in these sensational reads.

You can't find a better mind,
7 books in one series, what a stupendous mind!

Kathryn Leeming (11)
Painsley Catholic High School

Sam Hankinson's Mind

My thoughts are like a madman's mind
Thoughts enter my head like a fast car
I daydream about anything but girls, argh!
I wonder if one day I will go out with a girl
But I won't like her.
I talk to myself (in my brain) but the thoughts are like racing cars
So I get my words in a scramble.
I'm always thinking about surfing and fast cars
It is like I can't do work
Because I'm always thinking of fast cars and surfing.
But my thoughts are like fast cars, like Formula One and others
Just like a madman's brain.

Sam Hankinson (11)
Painsley Catholic High School

J K Rowling

Clever, clever J K Rowling,
Has a great imagination,
Harry Potter! Harry Potter!
What was her inspiration?

She made reading exciting
And sometimes even funny
Because her plots were so enchanting,
She made herself pots of money.

She's done such a lot and is ever so clever,
I really do think you will find
Compared with the rest with all of her brain power,
I would say she's a really great mind.

Hannah Williams (11)
Painsley Catholic High School

Trench Life

Oh to be home with my mum's lovely baking
Pies and pastries, just there for the taking.

In all of this madness I think of my home
All of us are going and I'm not alone.

Mud, sweat, blood and tears,
The trenches are full and not just with fears.

Tonight we're going, there's no way to stop,
We're up and we're at 'em, we're over the top.

Over the top and out with our gun
Soldiers are falling, no one has won.

Elizabeth Whitehouse (11)
Painsley Catholic High School

Books By Jacqueline Wilson

Jacqueline Wilson is funny and witty,
Lola Rose is a girl who moves to the city
The best book is 'Bad Girls' which is a real good scream,
Violet is a girl who's obsessed with Casper Dream.

Tracy Beaker is an orphan who likes to be cool,
In the sequel 'The Dare Game' she's naughty and bunks off school.

'Secrets' is the story of two girls who are worlds apart
While 'Treasure' strives for pleasure
It is always at India's leisure.

Jacqueline Wilson writes with understanding
Which makes her readers more demanding
Jacqueline Wilson will always walk tall
Jacqueline Wilson the *greatest mind of all!*

Laura Stevenson (11)
Painsley Catholic High School

Paula Radcliffe

Here comes Paula Radcliffe
Running down the track,
Gold is in her clutches,
She's never looking back.
She's a world class athlete
Who'll go down in history,
Not just for the medals she's won,
But her work for charity.
She's an idol for all,
From old to small
And one thing that you'll find,
Records have been rewritten,
She's changed sport in Britain
And she's truly a great mind!

Robbie Ryan (12)
Painsley Catholic High School

Michael Owen

A pacey forward, a scoring machine,
Michael Owen was in my dream,
He scored in every match
And there wasn't a catch.

When he was younger
He inspired me
To play football
After my tea.

I would go to the park
With all my mates
To play football
And the goals were great.

I loved to watch him
On the TV,
I hope and hope
That he will meet me.

Mark Long (11)
Painsley Catholic High School

My Pet Jaguar

His name is Coal,
He is as black as night,
He is fast and protective,
Although cuddly and cute,
He is loveable and happy,
But confident and sharp,
He has eyes like the sun
And spear-sharp claws,
He eats so much chocolate,
He has energy 24/7.

Jodie Brown (12)
Painsley Catholic High School

Muhammad Ali

He moves like a butterfly
He stings like a bee,
He'd hit you five times then you couldn't see.
He can't be beaten.
He's quick on his feet.
His blood pumping
His hands are thumping.
Fighting for freedom
Winning for pride.
He's got the mind of a winner
And the heart of a lion.
He's the champ,
He's Ali.

David Daniels (14)
Painsley Catholic High School

Florence Nightingale

She dressed mainly all in white.
Walking the wards in the night.
She'd hold their hands and pat their heads,
She straightened the covers and made the beds.
From bed to bed she went
Over the sick she lent,
She'd look after them all
Whether they were big or small.
Not only did she help those dying
She also helped the ones were are crying.
Florence Nightingale was like a friend
Because she stayed with you right to the end.

Hayley Fearn (14)
Painsley Catholic High School

Muhammad Ali

Muhammad Ali
He floats like a butterfly
And stings like a bee.
One day he found out he had Parkinson's Disease
It put him weak on his knees,
Now everyone sees
He was the best fighter
On land and at sea.
He still is a fighter
He's fighting disease,
He may not be a boxer ever again
But he doesn't have to be
Because people still fear his name.

Daniel Goodwin (14)
Painsley Catholic High School

The Computer Man

The richest man alive,
The best inventor of all time,
With state of the art computers,
Bill Gates changed all our lives.

His state of the art computers,
Became the windows of the world,
Bill Gates caused the world to step up a gear
And made it revolutionised.

Computers make the world go round
And the future to go on,
The best inventor of all time,
Bill Gates the computer man.

Jack Pauley (11)
Painsley Catholic High School

Amy Keates' Mind!

My thoughts are like a dream
They fill my heart with a gleam.
All day I daydream
I've always wondered if I'll be in a team.

I dream all day, I dream all night,
I can't help dreaming till morning light.
I dream about my bed
It's like Heaven, I dream about me
When I first turned eleven.

Amy Keates (11)
Painsley Catholic High School

Stanley Matthews

Stanley Matthews inspired alot.
He earned the name 'wizard of the dribble'.
Born in Hanley where he became great.
He tried and tried until the battle was won.
Never gave up until the match was won.
No doubt at all the best player in the world.
He got Stoke City promoted
And was later named Sir Stanley the great.

Sam Bennett (11)
Painsley Catholic High School

The Sea Is A Shark

The sea is a shark moving out
When it is hungry, it eats everything
That is in its path
Just like a shark.

Joseph Sullivan (12)
Painsley Catholic High School

The Sea

The sky was a ball of dough
With white spots surrounding it.
Turning over like a spaceman in space
Floating around the world.

With smoke and fumes polluting the fresh air
Snow every winter and sun every summer
As birds flying high, birds flying low,
Swoop over our heads.

Rebekah Lewis (12)
Painsley Catholic High School

My Grandma's Famous Bread

My grandma makes first class bread
'It's the best ever!' once I said.
Applying butter, flour, water and yeast,
It's ready to eat in minutes at least.
It has a fine, rich, creamy taste,
I scoff it in seconds, none gone to waste,
After I lick my lips, until they're fuzzy and sore
Just hoping and asking to have even more.

Rachel Wilson (11)
Painsley Catholic High School

The Sea

The sea is a roaring lion
That eats everything in its path.
The waves are its mouth
When it gets angry
It becomes a tidal wave
It destroys everyone.

Callum McGuire (12)
Painsley Catholic High School

Princess Diana

Diana! Princess Of Wales
Her life journey came to a halt
A tragic tear will mark this sorrowful day
As cherubims carry her to Heaven
But Diana's spirit remains with us.

She understood the needs of people at the end of their lives,
Her enduring commitment to people in bereavement
To ease other's impending death
For relief from physical pain as well as the need for love
Resolution and peace of mind.

Kamurai Wabatagore (14)
Painsley Catholic High School

My World

I look at the stars, they look like diamonds and crystals.
What would it be like to be a real star?
Would it be like a vase on a shelf that hasn't been moved for years?
I would like to be something bright and beautiful
Like a flower that never dies or a rainbow that never fades away.
Will my fantasies ever come true?
Will anyone ever believe me?
Will they laugh and joke like a pack of hyenas?
I sit and wonder, *what will be my destiny?*

Lauren Searcy (11)
Painsley Catholic High School

The Shark

The sea is rough and the waves are crashing against the rock.
The sea is a shark looking for food
It devours everything in its path.

Lewis Roberts (12)
Painsley Catholic High School

My Mum

M y mum is brill, I love her very much
Y ou just can't not love her, even when she's in a mood.

M y mum is brill, I love her very much,
U ltra inventive and makes yummy, scrummy food,
M y mum is brill, I love her very much.

I love my mum very much because she's brill.
S he's called Sarah Jane Stewart but I haven't got a middle name.

B rilliant she might be but always fussed about mess!
R inging, moaning about what I've done,
I love my mum so very much, she looked at a horse and
L ovingly bought him, so I gave her a big
L oving hug! I love my mum! She's a brill mind!

Cinnamon Stewart (11)
Painsley Catholic High School

My Mum

My mum is always there,
To always help and care.

When we go shopping together,
We 'shop until we drop'!
My mummy is the best,
You never know what she will wear next.
Her clothes are so trendy
But, only when she is with me!
She pays for everything I need,
I don't know any cook that feeds me,
Better than *my mum!*

My mum is always there,
To always help and care.

Grace Marlow (11)
Painsley Catholic High School

My Thoughts

My mind is like a stomach,
Always churning ideas around.

Thoughts enter my head like a jack-in-the-box,
Never knowing when they are going to pop up.

Every morning while in bed, I think about school,
School is like a rain cloud, dark, dull and horrible.

Every day while I stand in the playground I think about Christmas,
Christmas is like a fairytale, enchanting and magical.

Every day while I walk to school I think about my friends,
My friends are like the circus, they all have different talents.

My mind is like a stomach,
Always churning ideas around.

Sarah Thorley (12)
Painsley Catholic High School

The Aeroplane

An aeroplane is a giant bird
It hits the clouds as hard as it can
It swallows everything in its path
And there is nothing left where it had been.

Henry Heaton (12)
Painsley Catholic High School

The Volcano

The volcano is a roaring lion with a short temper.
It will not give you a chance if you mess with it.
The big red mouth is sizzling and snapping
Wanting you, to get its revenge.

Oliver Drew
Painsley Catholic High School

Art

Art is cool,
Art is fine.
Artists are amazing,
Artists like Jim Dine.

Art comes in all shapes and sizes,
Different colours, different emotion.
Feelings of love, sorrow and joy,
Even feelings of devotion.

Dali was a mad painter,
He painted melting clocks.
People in Dali's time
Thought his head was made of blocks.

Modigliani wasn't so mad,
But he drew elongated faces.
He made the noses really long,
Stretching things in different places.

The Egyptians wrote in pictures,
These symbols were called hieroglyphic.
The Chinese used watercolour,
That is why I think it's terrific.

But my most favourite of all,
Is the Impression: Sunrise, by Monet.
I like it because it has a sense of mystery
And it also makes my day.

Art is cool,
Art is fine.
Art is amazing,
Art is just divine.

Heather Moreton (13)
Painsley Catholic High School

Great Minds, Great Times

Great minds are common today,
There are some geniuses in the world, that's easy to say,
Politicians, scientists too,
Vaccines and medicines for me and you.

Lots of great minds, lots of great things,
Like Mozart the musician for the way he sings,
Like prime ministers, war generals too,
Leading an army it's not an easy thing to do.

Lots of great minds, lots of great times,
Like me for example for writing in rhymes,
Like Nelson Mandela and Martin Luther King,
For uniting all races, a beautiful thing.

Great minds are everywhere,
The Wright brothers, for transportation in the air,
Steven Spielberg for bringing us excitement on the screen,
ET, Jurassic Park, the films we've all seen.

Joshua Wilcox (13)
Painsley Catholic High School

Great Minds

There was a man called Isaac Newton
For some strange reason he lived in Lutton.
His nickname was Wutton.
When he was a child he did his homework
But never did his housework.
His mother told him to eat his greens
But instead he thought and dreamed.
He loved to play with dolls
But his friends thought he played with poles.
So when he was older he had a great mind
And everyone knew he was right.

Natalie Ralphs (14)
Painsley Catholic High School

Great Minds

What are great minds?
People who manipulate the world
With their thoughts and actions.
Enveloping the world with new ideas.
Shaping the world we live in.
Great minds.

Great minds that think alike,
Unite the nations of the world.
A new sense of purpose born
When two minds differ the world divides.
The seams of friendship torn apart.
Great minds.

Who are great minds?
Isaac Newton; the gravity master,
Shakespeare; the manipulator of thought
Winston Churchill; a great leader.
All great minds.

As I sit here now and think with my mind.
I wonder, one day, what if,
Will I, my mind, what will I be,
Will I be a great mind?

Samuel Mellor (13)
Painsley Catholic High School

Women's Minds Reach To Freedom

Suffragettes and Emily Pankhurst are synonymous,
Many of the women are anonymous.
Do women of today know the women of last century died to give
the vote
And freedom for women to live life without fear?
Pankhurst was the mind to motivate,
Pankhurst was the mind to suffragettes creating scenes,
One died for their cause, throwing herself under a racing horse.

Claire Fallows (12)
Painsley Catholic High School

Athletic Minds

Her nerves build up furiously,
The audience waits curiously.
A new challenge is on the way,
Will Kelly Holmes' courage manage to stay?

The whistle is blown,
Her great power is shown.
As she starts the race with might,
Her mind calls, *you shall win this fight.*

Her legs run their best,
As she begins to beat the rest.
The crowd desperately hope,
That she will manage to cope.

The end has finally drawn,
There is a winner born.
Kelly has beaten them all,
She didn't fall, she stood tall.

Tightly her hands hold,
The well-deserved gold.
Her smile is full of triumph and pride,
Her great mind she cannot hide!

Chloe Whilock (13)
Painsley Catholic High School

Friends

I have two very special friends,
I think we'll be friends till the end.
There is Zoe who is very funny,
Then there's Hannah who is very specky.
They are both really friendly,
Or else they wouldn't be my special friends.
Hannah is quite tall, Zoe is quite small.
They are my very special, special friends.

Rebecca Prime (12)
Painsley Catholic High School

My Dog

Walking swiftly,
Sniffing as she goes.
Short tail pointing,
Searching as she does.

Spots an object,
Fur stands on end,
Starts to shake at it,
Foe or friend.

Deep growls from within
Rumbling throaty sounds,
She pulls on her lead
I get pulled on the ground.

Just a foot tall
But as strong as an ox,
Pulls again and growls
But it's just an empty box.

Poppy Holland (12)
Painsley Catholic High School

Autumn Days

Leaves are falling off the trees,
Splashing in puddles up to your knees,
Having a cuddle by the fire
Looking at the church spire.

Ready to go to bed
Cuddling up to my teddy bear, Fred!
In the morning I awake,
To see the coloured leaves on the lake.

I run outside to go and play
Jumping in the leaves on the way,
Conkers falling to the ground,
Squirrels jumping with a bound.

Michelle Richardson (12)
Painsley Catholic High School

My Brother

My brother is definitely the best,
He's better than all the rest,
Who will do anything any day,
To help me on my way!

He has his music booming,
In his car he will be zooming,
He cruises round in his car
And never realises he has gone too far!

Sometimes he can be annoying,
Others he will be boring,
But at the end of the day,
What I have to say is,
'Hey! That's my brother!'

Sadie Golden (12)
Painsley Catholic High School

Sad!

There are lots of things that make me sad
But some things make me really mad.
One of the things are boys,
They think that cars are toys.
Another thing is school
All the teachers are so cruel,
We get bossed around all day
Then they make us stay.
The classrooms are so dull
They teach us until we're full.
I hate things that make me mad,
It makes me very, very sad.

Hannah Shenton (12)
Painsley Catholic High School

William Shakespeare

Shakespeare was the writer of his day,
He wrote many a sonnet
And many a play.

Through the reign of Elizabeth,
From 'Caesar' to 'Midsummer Night's Dream',
From 'King Lear' to 'Macbeth'.

'Hamlet' was all doom and gloom,
'Taming Of The Shrew' was funny,
'The Merchants' play saw Portia bloom,
'Much Ado' was sunny.

Thirty seven plays in all,
Plus many sonnets and verse,
He played them all out in Swan's Hall
And became every school kid's curse.

Rhys Spooner (12)
Painsley Catholic High School

Mad Monsters

Boys are monsters through and through
Irritate me and anger you.
They always want to be the top
And never know just when to stop.
They kick a football, scream and shout
They have no brains, there is no doubt.
Behind a thing that they call pride
Their feelings they will always hide.
The other problem with the boys
Is that they think all cars are toys.
God if you're listening, hear my plea,
Don't make those boys, make girls like me!

Zoë Fallows (12)
Painsley Catholic High School

Inside My Mind

My mind is like a wild tiger because sometimes it's out of control.
Thoughts enter my head like a flash of lightning, such as my cat.

My cat is like a small ball of fluff just waiting to pop out,
She is so soft that she is like a cotton bud.

My family makes me so happy that I'm like the sun,
Bursting with brightness and warmness all around me.

I wonder about my homework and it makes me feel so down,
It feels like I'm falling down a well.

I wonder about my school work and it's like seagulls at break,
Never stopping, always coming.

My mind drifts to food which makes me feel so hungry,
I'm like a lioness when it's just been given a chunk of meat.

My mind is like a wild tiger because sometimes it's out of control.

Cathryn Button (12)
Painsley Catholic High School

Armstrong On The Moon

Neil Armstrong, the man that landed on the moon.
How courageous he was getting on that rocket
For him to help us know what the moon was like.
How proud he must have been standing there, heard and seen.
The power he must have had,
Having the privilege to be the first man on the moon.
What a gloom came off his face of the courageous man Neil
Armstrong.
How determined he was to get to the moon
To show everyone that he's very proud.
He's come back from his journey to show everybody
How outstanding and how devoted he was to that very mission.

Steven Wareham (12)
Painsley Catholic High School

Michael Schumacher

Michael, Michael, it's his name,
Driving, driving is his game.
Michael wins again and again,
Faster and faster, it's insane.
Michael has a driving brother,
It's a threat but he still wins another.
After winning seven times,
He drives just like he mimes.

Michael, Michael, it's his name,
Driving, driving is his game.
Michael wins again and again,
Faster and faster, it's insane.
Michael has a driving team,
Keeping ahead full of steam.
Michael stood as a warning,
But is he just yawning?
Oh Michael! It's just a cycle.

Ben Mothershaw (13)
Painsley Catholic High School

My Mind

My mind is like a plant, it grows every day.
Thoughts enter my head like a bullet from a gun.
I think the PS2 is like the Earth, I'm always on it.
My mind drifts to homework, I think of it as love
Because it is always being given to me.
I think about the TV, it's like my heart
I can't live without it.
I wonder about my dog which is just like a flower
If it isn't fed it dies.
I think of clothes as a book cover
Always covering up what you are.
My mind is like a plant, it grows every day.

Luke Adams (13)
Painsley Catholic High School

Neil Armstrong

N eil is the man for the job, brave and courageous.
E very day he trains hard, building up to the big moment.
I magining the moment Neil gets a little anxious.
L aughing away with his mates, but what if he never comes back!

A rrives the big day and the main man is having some last minute
    doubts.
R ocket's ready, roaring to go, so is mission control.
M ission control to base, everything is up to standard,
    we're ready to take off.
S tart the engines 5, 4, 3, 2, 1, blast-off!
T he boosters are on, the rocket's moving,
    then in a flash it shot up and away.
R eady to build up speed to break through the atmosphere.
O ff drops the special booster to get us through the sound barrier.
N eil slides down the ladder and says,
    'It's one small step for man, but one giant leap for mankind.'
G ravity is now on our side as we race back to Earth.

Alex Jones (12)
Painsley Catholic High School

Poem Of My Mum

My mum is the greatest,
She works ten hours a day,
She is very hopeful
And gets very good pay.

My mum is the greatest,
She is proud of what she's done
And brave, and anxious,
To carry on for so long.

My mum is the greatest,
She's done her masters degree,
She helps lots of people,
But mostly *me!*

Daniel Ward (13)
Painsley Catholic High School

Chloe

Chloe is my little dog,
Cavalier is her breed.
She is a little hog,
As she eats up all her feed.

Her coat is soft and silky,
She really is a pet.
The white is pale and milky,
The black is dark as jet.

I wonder what she's thinking,
As she curls up by my feet.
She dreams she's rabbit chasing,
As she paddles with her feet.

She's like a wolf when she howls,
At the doorbell when it rings.
It's funny when she growls,
She must think that she sings.

She really is the best pet,
And I'd never let her go.
I hope she's never upset,
Because I love her so.

Rachel Sedgwick (12)
Painsley Catholic High School

Saladin

S aracens marching down the hill,
A ll the crusaders to pay the bill,
L ords to kill,
A round the hill,
D one and dusted,
I t meant that they were busted,
N ow around the hill.

Patrick Walters (12)
Painsley Catholic High School

Christmas Time!

I love the Christmas season
It carries in the air
Everybody's freezing
But there's still chattering everywhere.
It's really, really cosy when you're just sitting by the fire
You could watch the soaps all day and you'd never begin to tire.

I love to go sing carols at everybody's door
There's loads of different kinds
Everybody seems to want more, more, more
Those are the really good times.
You can put up decorations
And then see all of your relations.

I love to open presents
And start a brand new year
For dinner you might have pheasant
And hold your family dear.
Hot chocolate I like to drink
As I rest with time to think.

I love the Christmas season
It carries in the air
Everybody's freezing
But there's still chattering everywhere.
It's really, really cosy when you're just sitting by the fire
You could watch the soaps all day and you'd never begin to tire.

Rebecca Ward (12)
Painsley Catholic High School

My Mind In The Classroom

'I'm very cross with you, ignorant child!'
She boomed, standing before me.
'Look at me when I'm talking to you!'
Not my fault, school just bores me.

I've tried to listen,
I've tried to learn,
I've tried and tried,
But nothing works.

I like to set my imagination free,
Give a rest to my poor mind,
I like to go to far off places,
Leave the classroom behind.

As I looked up to her face,
I imagined her eyes fire-red,
Then I noticed her snappy suit,
Some fun with clothes instead.

I dressed her in a stripy shirt,
The kind they wear in France,
And of course, to match her eyes,
I added some spotty pants.

I giggled and laughed at her new look,
The one she failed to see,
She opened her mouth, I stopped in horror,
Another detention for me . . .

Alexandra Foulkes (12)
Painsley Catholic High School

Great Minds

Great minds discover great finds.
From steam trains to jet planes,
Scientist, poets,
Leaders, composers, all kinds,
Doctors, writers, philosophers,
Too many to mention at times.
We are grateful for their work,
In so many different ways,
Saving lives, space travel,
To entertainment we unravel.
What would life be like without them?
Some more great than others,
Others more famous than some.
What is the secret of their success?
That is something I have yet to overcome.

Katrina Earley (12)
Painsley Catholic High School

J K Rowling

Five years ago, nobody knew her
The books were a twinkle in her eye
Full of imagination and magical words
Harry was an unknown guy.

She made magic wizards fun again
Her characters brought magic to you
Amazing stories of surprise and friendship
And a car that gracefully flew.

Now books line shelves across the UK
And a billion pounds line her pocket
She's rich beyond her wildest dreams,
Her sales continue to rocket!

Becky Hickey (12)
Painsley Catholic High School

Churchill

C hurchill won us the prestigious war,
H is wealth turned into fame.
U nder pressure he fought against Germany,
R ich and wealthy.
C onflict commenced and victory was claimed.
H itler was unthoughtful, and wasn't wise,
I n great shame, Hitler lost.
L ittle Churchill I'm sure was proud!
L ike a football coach when he won!

Luke Finney (11)
Painsley Catholic High School

Freedom

W hen knowing you can do what you want, when you want
                                    and how you want
H aving the support to make you feel safe but for you to also
                                    know you are free
A sking questions and knowing you are not going to be lied to
T aking time out to do things for *you* and not for the benefit of others

I nvoking others to think of their surroundings
S ailing across the ocean in a schooner with no boundaries
                                    to hold you back

F eeling the softness of sand skimming across the soles of your feet
R ecognising the ability to speak without being silenced
E xpressing your feelings and knowing no one is going to say
                                    or do anything about it
E nergy to move wherever you wish
D oing things that you would normally do
O pening your eyes to the beautiful world in front of you
M aking sure you are doing no harm but are feeling good
    about yourself.

Freedom - what does it mean to you?

Philippa Pointon (14)
St Joseph's College

Freedom

W orkloads get you down, two hours of homework a night,
E veryone asks you to do better; I am not that bright.

H alf the population is poor and uneducated,
A country has too little food and it is completely over populated,
V eterans of war are not praised for their pain and trouble,
E ventually their dead bodies forgotten will sink into the soil.

N o more at home and in school can we ever be free?
O ur lives are controlled by rules about uniform, taking our dignity.

F ar too any people rely on the way they look alone,
R hinoplastic and facelift to make them a celebrity clone,
E ven today, the age of 'love and peace' there is still racism,
E nd this now, but after all this prejudice can this world be forgiven?
D on't rule my life and tell me where to go and how I should act,
O nly I should choose where I am able o go, give me just
                                                    a little respect,
M ake the most of your life, there might not be much of it left!

Stephanie Lakin (13)
St Joseph's College

Freedom

F reedom to me is a beautiful beach, when the sun sets in the sky
R oaming freely about the land, running through fields and streams,
    with no worries whatsoever.
E verybody free to be who they are, making the world a more
    genuine, happy place to live.
E nough of rules and regulations, stopping individuality, everyone
    free to express their opinions.
D oing whatever comes into your head, with no one saying it's wrong
    and telling you what you should be doing and how you should be
    doing it.
O f all these things the best would be, freedom to be friends with
    who I want and seeing them when I want to, the people I love all
    around me, getting on well together, not ashamed of who they are.
M oney not important and material things matter to no one.

Francesca Jones (13)
St Joseph's College

Freedom

F reedom is to explore, to be set loose from all boundaries,
R etreat from a world full of hatred and disrespect.
E nvelope myself in a world of calm serenity,
E scape from racism, white is not perfect.
D reamin' dreams then living them out,
O pinionate myself without being criticised.
M ost importantly of all . . .
    To have no rules so I can't break them.

Róisín Bartlam (13)
St Joseph's College

Freedom

F reedom to do what I want when I want to
R eactions don't apply
E ndurance is the only thing that will stop me
E verything is mine to try
D anger can't stop me
O ver and under nothing can stop me
M y friends all around me.

Matthew Bailey (13)
St Joseph's College

Freedom

F reedom to me is a beautiful beach with palm trees blowing
                                               in the wind.
R unning water trickling gently down to the beautiful blue sea.
E verybody smiling sweetly and no malice in the world.
E ach different face beaming with glee.
D oing whatever we want to do with no restrictions or consequences.
O pportunties to be the best that we can be.
M aking the most of our potential.

Daniel Taylor (14)
St Joseph's College

Freedom

Buying lots of Jimmy Choos,
Not to forget Prada shoes.

Being able to accomplish your eternal dream,
While eating strawberries and cream.

Being able to go where you wish,
And getting everything you deserve on a dish.

Going on an amazing shopping spree,
And having my own Chinese chef called Ching Lee.

Having a wardrobe for Louis Vuitton bags,
Being able to catch up with all the celeb gossip from mags.

Going every year to the MTV Awards,
And sitting at cricket matches with the lords.

Not being pointed at for being yourself,
Not being left out like an odd toy on its own shelf.

Overall being happy,
Which means money growing on my trees.
This is freedom for me.

Rajvir Sangha (13)
St Joseph's College

Freedom

F reedom is a tiger roaming free
R oaring with joy over the Serengeti
E very bird travels the sky
E agles know true freedom as they soar up high
D angerous is freedom, if given too much
O ver the skies birds go places we long to touch
M y view of freedom is plain to see, I want freedom all for me.

Imran Pirmohamed (13)
St Joseph's College

Jets

Jets are fast
Jets can fly
They look brill
Way up high

They are cool
They are smart
I love them
With all my heart

They are loud
They fly so high
They could even
Go past the sky

Now this is the end
Of my poem
I've told you about jets
So now I'm going.

James Thorley (11)
St Thomas More Catholic College

Hallowe'en

This night is really scary
Some people are brown and hairy
The things from outer space are taking over this spooky place
Stay away from vampire bats
Because they'll eat your favourite cats
Keep your cars away from Frankenstein
'Cause he'll gobble them up before the end of this rhyme
Because it's Hallowe'en.

Calum Edwards (12)
St Thomas More Catholic College

She Isn't Small

She isn't small,
She isn'thin,
But that doesn't matter,
It's what lies within.

She copies and she creeps,
She screams and she weeps,
Who cares about that,
She's here and she's here for keeps.

Although she is cheeky,
She's really not that freaky,
For now she is kinda cool,
Remember though, I'm the one who rules.

She drives me up the wall,
And thinks that I'm always at her beckoning call,
But even though she's like a ten-foot pole,
She's my sister and her name is Nicole.

Katie Louise Jones (13)
St Thomas More Catholic College

The Flower Seller

The flower seller stood
On the corner trying to sell her flowers
She stood a very long time
It was nearly eight hours
She tried her best just like the rest
But couldn't sell a flower
It was raining all day
She earned no pay
Now she's got a basket of dead flowers.

Gemma Cammillare (13)
St Thomas More Catholic College

Seasons Of The Year

Winter

Snow is falling all around
Soon it will be white all over the ground
Children build snowmen tall
Sliding on the snow and sometimes fall
Snowball fights between girls and boys
Soon it will be time to open their toys
Christmas presents lie under the tree
Children shriek and shout with glee.

Spring

The new season is spring
When the birds start to sing
Sometimes we'll have small showers
But this will help grow all the flowers
As spring goes on it's warm and calm
All the new animals are born on the farm
Especially the new spring lambs born to the ewes
And now new names we've got to choose.

Summer

Summer comes when it's nice and hot
People sunbathing in a nice, warm spot
When it's hot and the sun comes out
Going on holiday out and about
We go away to have some fun
And to enjoy, the lovely sun
Going on holiday to a faraway place
Everybody with a happy, smiling face.

Autumn

As summer goes and the sun fades down
Autumn turns the leaves golden-brown
Then there will come a gentle breeze
Blowing leaves to leave bare trees
Then they will fall all around
Covering every inch of the ground
Conkers growing and falling in their shell
Children collecting, shout and yell.

Roxanne Wilton (11)
St Thomas More Catholic College

Animals And Mammals

Animals are cute,
Some are scary,
Some are fat,
Others are hairy.
Fish are scaly,
Frogs are smooth,
Mice squeak,
I could go on for the whole week.
Dogs bark,
Cats miaow,
Fish live in water,
My guinea pig had a daughter.
Rabbits hop,
Cheetahs run,
Faster than a bullet out of a gun.
Out of all the animals and mammals listed there . . .
I have one more to add,
Dolphins are my favourite,
They are always happy,
Never sad . . .
They do nothing bad!

Laura Rickard (12)
St Thomas More Catholic College

My Friend

When the night has gone elsewhere,
The morning breaks with clear blue skies,
My friend is here, jolly and bright,
Without my friend the day is bleak,
The warmth of him touches within,
We are able to do things,
Things we cannot do without my friend,
Take gentle strolls around the park,
Or ride our bikes on journeys far,
We are able to sit, to have picnics,
To visit the seaside where we have fun,
Strange; when my friend has gone to sleep,
There is no laughing, talking, people,
Not only do we need my friend,
But animals and plants too,
His golden coat shines so brightly,
His rays of light keep us warm,
He tries his best to please us all,
But isn't here some days of the year,
For he is fighting against big, black clouds,
My friend will always be here,
Can you guess who he is?

Answer the sun.

Chloe Ball (13)
St Thomas More Catholic College

Trick Or Treat

We all set off at six o'clock
Knocking on all doors
Trick or treat we always say
And it's sweets they give away
Running round the streets at night
Our mission is to scare
But most of the time we scare ourselves
With the masks we always wear.

Richard Tranah (12)
St Thomas More Catholic College

Christmas Joy

Christmas is coming
People are humming
People are happy
People are chatty
People are excited
People are shouting through the streets
Some people are about to meet
As they get out of bed for their morning treat
When the kids go downstairs
Surprise, surprise, there's presents there
Kids opening their presents on a Saturday Christmas morning
Just as the beautiful day is dawning
Wooden toys and shiny dolls
Lovely food and chimney bells.

Matthew Keeling (13)
St Thomas More Catholic College

Christmas Night

On Christmas night,
Santa Claus came from a great height.
He came to bring the toys
For all the girls and boys.
It was snowing outside
So all the children went to hide.
I was watching him place the presents under the tree,
He chuckled at a bee,
Then he saw me.
He ran upstairs and chased me,
He said, 'Get to bed,
Or you won't have that toy ted.'

Lisa Darlington (13)
St Thomas More Catholic College

Horror Hotel

Horror Hotel, Horror Hotel
The rooms are as dark as cells
The staff there are spooky
They never offer no cookie
I hear a scream
Just like in my dream
Horror Hotel, Horror Hotel

Horror Hotel, Horror Hotel
The main feature is the poisoned well
The well had been cast under a spell
When someone had fell
In the back garden there were graves
I heard the wind, whistling waves
Horror Hotel, Horror Hotel.

James Clarke (11)
St Thomas More Catholic College

Music And Me

Music makes me happy
Music makes me angry
Music makes me want to go skating
Music makes me want to do something

Some music is cool
My sort of music is rock
I read when listening to music
Music is who I am

Some music makes me sleepy
Some music makes me sad
Some music makes me bored
Some music creeps me out.

Adam Foster (13)
St Thomas More Catholic College

The Great War

All over the trenches, the winding trenches
Lie the bodies of soldiers,
The living can hardly move for death, death, death.

I'm shooting next to an American,
Our guns bang as we shoot together.
A bullet finds my new friend,
He sees it and he falls to the floor,
His eyes as wide as the bullet.

He flies back as it hits his shoulder,
He splats in the watery mud.
I go to help him from my firing step,
However, I feel my first footstep sink.
I'm helpless as he sinks too.
One more body to stride over,
One more friend lost.

I sit on my step and look around,
People pound into the ground,
The only sight is death.

Lee Finch (13)
St Thomas More Catholic College

If You Could Be

If you could be anything, what would you be?

I'd be a dandelion swaying in the summer breeze,
I'd be a bird gently flying in the autumn sky,
I would be an explorer finding out life's many mysteries,
But I'd rather be myself because my life is ace.

Lewis Kenny (11)
St Thomas More Catholic College

This World

What's in this world today?
We live in a land of fear.
Countries at war, people at war,
We all hope for improvement.

Anti-this, anti-that, save the something!
What should we worry about?
Who should we worry about?
It's our choice for the future.

Is this life really as it seems?
Do we live in fear of nothing?
We will never know the answer.
So many secrets hidden.

This world of ours, this world.

Liam Dobson (13)
St Thomas More Catholic College

Disaster Zone

I was born in a disaster zone,
and have always lived alone.
I have scavenged looking for loot,
only to get the great boot.

I always wanted to have get togethers,
but the sound of bombs are like that of feathers.
We have always had horrible weather,
but people like me don't bother.

I was born in a disaster zone,
and I have become one.
The disaster zone has won,
and it's not long before dawn . . .

Kenneth Iredia (13)
St Thomas More Catholic College

The Future

What has this world come to -
If it carries on like this?
All the wars and the disagreements
Will our lives be worth living?

The future is a funny thing
It knows how we shall end,
For all I can do is live for the present,
And death could be around the next bend.

Will the world ever be at peace?
No! Is what the majority say.
But there is a minority who have the hope,
That we can be safe, some day.

Everything, we wonder about,
Has the future already decided.
The things that we all hope for?
The things that we have sighted.

Now what can we do but sit and wait?
What the future holds -
Ever for me.

Thomas Edwards (13)
St Thomas More Catholic College

Christmas

The tinsel glitters
The lights twinkle
The baubles shine
While Christmas Day goes on
Christmas presents wait to be unwrapped
While my dad sets up the camera
My mum's making dinner
And my brothers and I eat our sweets.
Finally we open our presents to see what we have got.

Teresa Brammer (12)
St Thomas More Catholic College

Pain And Joy

Guns growling, bombs booming,
Faces falling to the ground.
Gas floating, making no sound.
Dead bodies slowly rot,
Grown men screaming in agony.

Men still fighting
Hurt men sighing,
Bits of humans all around,
I can see them on the ground.

Guns not growling, bombs not booming,
People are assuming
The war is now over,
'Hip hip hooray!'
I hear the soldiers say.

Jade Bentley (14)
St Thomas More Catholic College

Bonfire Night

On the 5th of November the crowds gather
People laughing and screaming
The fireworks rapidly going up into the sky
You hear a cheer and a great big bang.

The crowds gaze at the magnificent colours
And the fantastic shapes and sizes
The rides spinning and twirling
The people eagerly dive on
And enjoy this fabulous night.

Amanda Preece (13)
St Thomas More Catholic College

Confronting The Enemy

I sat there in my dugout
Listening to the bombs being dropped
In the open spaces around me.
Hearing the guns spitting at the enemy,
I'm hiding away because I don't want to fight.

All around me is thick mud, sucking me underground,
towards Hell.
I'm scared and I don't want to go there
And I don't want to fight.
But suddenly I'm awakened by the call
Of my soldier friend -
His helpless scream echoes through the trench
And I am on call.

I scramble to my feet, dragging my equipment,
It's weighing me down. It's as heavy as an elephant.
I climb the steps, they seem to come in their millions.
As I reach the top I look over the field,
There are people shouting for help with deafening tones.
And dead bodies, covered in a red layer of paint blood,
I didn't know what I was letting myself in for
but oh well . . .
. . . crash!
. . . bang!
. . . dead!

Emma Jordan (13)
St Thomas More Catholic College

Quick, Mud, Honour

The trenches are like tunnels,
They are always dark and eerie.
But in the trenches where I stay
I can see the pain clearly.

The trenches are like tunnels,
The mud is sticky jam,
People always sink in it,
I save them if I can.

The trenches are like tunnels,
They don't always save me,
The bullets sting like bees,
Why do they want to kill me?

The trenches are like tunnels,
They're full of rotting limbs,
They're crawling with rats and worms,
The guilt in me squirms.

The trenches are like tunnels,
When there is death there is honour,
I'm going to die now . . .
In ultimate horror!

Jamie Coleman (13)
St Thomas More Catholic College

My Brother Benjamin

B is for boisterous
E is for enthusiastic and energetic
N is for natter, which my brother does all day long
J is for jumping
A is for ambition because he would die to be a footballer
M is for mysterious
 I is for initiative, which my brother sometimes uses
N is for nice, which *most* of the time he is.

Daniel Gooding (11)
St Thomas More Catholic College

True Love Hurts

I shiver when you hold my hand,
Your lips are like a rose, soft to the touch.
When you're not there, I miss you so much,
When I see you, there are butterflies in my stomach,
And when you went, the love turned into destruction.
My heart pounded like the hard beat of a drum,
The statue of you was tattooed into my heart.
And my heart became frozen, locking everything inside.
My mind became an ocean of memories,
My lips had forgotten the touch of a rose
My hand became withered
And I stayed alone, with no feeling in my heart
No emotion to be shown
As true love hurts.

Amy Ostrouchow (14)
St Thomas More Catholic College

The Snowman

One lump of snow upon the ground,
Then becomes a snowman,
With a carrot for a nose,
Two buttons for his eyes,
And a mouth made out of coal,
Two twigs for arms
And a scarf wrapped around his neck,
And a hat sat proudly on his head,
Out came the sun,
And all that was left of snowman was then a puddle of water,
Until next winter,
Of course!

Kate Harrington (12)
St Thomas More Catholic College

My Brother

I love my brother, he is so ace,
He's in a band and also plays bass.
Dave is sometimes cheeky,
He can also be very freaky.

Me and Dave are very close,
Because of this I always boast.
My love for Dave will never end
As long as he's got money that I can spend.

My big bro is such a dude
He also likes eating a lot of food
I think this just sums up my brother
If I don't go now, people will say I
Chat like my mother.

Zoe Wheat (13)
St Thomas More Catholic College

Autumn

Leaves falling,
Wind blowing,
Conkers dropping
From the trees.

Squirrels running,
Faster and faster
With the windy breeze.

Parents by the fireside,
Children tucked up in bed,
The flowers have even closed,
To look forward to the day ahead.

Kelsey Franklin (12)
St Thomas More Catholic College

The Beach

When we go to the beach,
Our teachers don't teach.
We have lots of fun,
Playing in the hot sun.
We build sandcastles,
And have skirts with tassles.
We have flags on top
And drink juicy pop.

We have ice cream
And work as a team.
We have to go on rides
Because of the tides.
We go into the shops
And I look at the tops.
Then we go and I feel really low.

Laura Hulme (13)
St Thomas More Catholic College

The House Of Doom

There was no smoke from the chimney
And there was no glass in the window
There was no stairs leading to the door
The rain smashed down on the floor
The house was very bitter and gloomy.

The garden did not look like it had been touched
And there was a grave in the back garden
There was sand before the grass
The rats smell of blood and rotting bodies
The garden was just as lifeless as the house itself.

Luke Melhado (11)
St Thomas More Catholic College

In The Trenches

In the trenches I lie
Trying to go to sleep
But I am thinking of my friends
Who had to die.

We have fought all day
For the little land we've gained
There are dead bodies everywhere
Being eaten by the rats.

My feet are dead
They are rotting and black
We have been on our feet all day
Trying to keep the Germans away.

I am going to sleep now
We don't know what tomorrow brings
Could it be victory and health -
Or could I die and lose everything?

Tom Keeling (14)
St Thomas More Catholic College

The Victorian Ground

As the remainders of the Victoria Ground lie in wait,
We remember the good times and the bad,
Matthews and Banks in goal and midfield,
They helped us win the Charity Shield.
Although they are now old and grey,
They are still in our hearts all the way,
The ground is now in pieces, broken and knocked down,
Yet we act as if it is still there,
When we tell people about the good times we had there,
When people went there not one of them would of frowned,
And that's the story of the Victoria Ground.

Mitchell Barnett (11)
St Thomas More Catholic College

The Dark War

Bodies litter the ground,
But the guns go on making that terrible sound.
Men weeping over lost limbs,
Their future looking extremely grim,
The rifles go stuttering on, as a man shouts,
'Look out! Bomb!'

The sun rises over the hills,
But all you can see, north, south,
East and west, is an ocean of bodies.
Trenches full of worried men waiting
For their lives to end.

Soldiers driven crazy by the scenes of war,
The conditions were very poor.
The war seems to go on and on
In an endless loop of time.

Matthew O'Rourke (13)
St Thomas More Catholic College

The Beautiful Game

It's all in the name, the blood
the fame, the sweat
the sheer pain
I run up the pitch
to feel the game
with the crowd chanting my name.

The ref blows his whistle
to start again
the battle commences
with the hope I can score
and not end the game
with a measly draw.

Conal O'Reilly (11)
St Thomas More Catholic College

Summer

Daffodils are coming
The trees are growing leaves
It's time to bathe in the sun
And the children are having fun.

The children are eating ice cream
In the red-hot sun

But now summer is going
And winter is coming so we say goodbye
For now and see you again.

Jake Harris (11)
St Thomas More Catholic College

Music

I like music with a catchy beat,
I like music that's up to date,
I like music that is great to sing,
I like music such as pop!

I hate music that's from years ago,
I hate music that is old fashioned,
I hate music from TV shows,
I hate music such as rock!

Charlotte Stubbs (13)
St Thomas More Catholic College

Little Red Fruit

Sweet and rosy like a cherry,
You've always been my angel.
Your presence ever makes me merry,
Little, round, juicy berry!

Rachel Titchener (17)
St Thomas More Catholic College

Haunted Memories

Confused thoughts,
That lay before me,
Piece together
The woman's story.

Past and present
The memories flash
Constant reminder
Life in his hands.

Dark and dingy
The haunted past
Ruling her life
And builds her story.

The way she lives
The constant fear
With her two hands
The end is here!

Amanda Kerr (17)
St Thomas More Catholic College

The Trenches

Bang! Was a normal sound
as shells were always going off
trying to hit the enemy, but never
even getting close.

Eeek! Was a normal sound
hundreds, even thousands of mice
eating everything they can sink
their teeth into, even the dead.

Silence is a normal sound
the dead lying motionless
as if asleep and not going
to wake up, just still and silent.

William Hilditch (13)
St Thomas More Catholic College

My Uncle

On the 24th August you slipped away from me,
All I can remember was the phone call
I shed many tears for you that night,
Wondering why?
Why? Why did you do what you did?
Did we do something wrong?
Why cause all this heartache?
I miss you more each day
I just want to see you again and
The smile which you gave.
When I see you again, up above the clouds
Please tell me why,
Why you took your life?
One year has passed
And I still shed the tears,
Even though you're not next to me
You're still in my heart.
Night-night Gary
I love and miss you
But I can't stop wondering why,
Why you took your life?

Hannah Powell (16)
St Thomas More Catholic College

Hallowe'en

Happy times go bad
All Hallow's Eve can make you sad
Lonely cold nights
Loud people trick or treating
Owls hunting for food
When everyone is sleeping
Evil things go a-creeping
Not only on Hallowe'en, but every day
                              of the year.

Elsa-Marie Evans (13)
St Thomas More Catholic College

The Tunnel

Strong glow in the distance,
deciding whether this light is safe.
I'm alone,
In a tunnel.
Its physical appearance is frightening,
but the tunnel feels like home.
For a second I'm shocked,
I'm back in reality, voices!
Annoying voices echoing!
In a flash I'm back again
In this tunnel.
I'm heading towards the light.
The atmosphere is soft, the light is safe,
I feel wonderful
As though this place is my destiny.
I am now complete, I've reached the light.
The calming yet wonderful atmosphere,
This is my destiny, I realise
As I enter the Pearly Gates of Heaven!

Sally Horton (15)
St Thomas More Catholic College

School Trips

You're all excited, raring to go,
But end up forgetting something,
Oh no!
When the coach has finally come,
It isn't really much fun.
To wait all day in the rain,
We all look like we're insane.
When we're there it isn't much fun,
But when it's finally time to go home.
Everyone has a great old moan,
And we end up having to go again.

Rebecca May Dudley (13)
St Thomas More Catholic College

Rugby

You sit in the changing room,
Waiting, anticipating what is lurking on the other side.
You step out the door, look at what
Will soon be doing their best to hurt you.
You step on to the field, look them in the eye,
Hoping, praying you will not be the first target.
Then it happens, you somehow end up with the ball.
You panic, all you see is that line,
It seems so far away,
Run, run is all you can hear.
You run so fast, with so much pace,
You dodge the killers with more haste,
Before you know it you're there,
You've done it,
Try.

Joseph Allen (15)
St Thomas More Catholic College

Hallowe'en

Hallowe'en is nearly here,
It's a scary time of the year.
Witches, ghosts, goblins too,
Pumpkin faces watching you.
Apple bobbing,
Children sobbing,
Hallowe'en is nearly here.
Torches flashing in the dark,
Scaring dogs and making them bark,
Trick or treat,
For a bag full of sweets,
Hallowe'en is nearly here.

Abbey Hopkinson (11)
St Thomas More Catholic College

Dark Walk

It's just dropped about 30 degrees,
I can't feel my fingers or my knees.
We sneak into this yard, smashed off the lock,
Tick-tock, what's this? We stand in sudden shock.
'It's OK lads, it's only the town hall clock.'
We're all paranoid now, full of fear,
All these quiet noises near.

We head on into the dark sky smoke,
Looking for something to do.
In this dark place my legs begin to shake,
This can't be me, I'm a fake.

Suddenly, this bright light shines down on me,
Might run, yes just might . . .
How lucky am I? It was only a security light.
I give up, I'm going, I run off into the dark night,
Not a thing in sight.

Patrick Hearne (14)
St Thomas More Catholic College

I Miss You

Memories of you I'll always have inside,
Pictures of you laughing, always in my mind
I remember the day you went away
There were things I wanted to do, some things I wanted to say
I was too young back then to fully understand
Why I couldn't be there to hold your hand
But now I know, now I see
It was just their way of protecting me.

Jodee Colclough (17)
St Thomas More Catholic College

Bonfire Night

All the sky was alive and bright,
Every colour could be seen, it was Bonfire Night,
Oranges, blues, red and greens,
Every colour in the sky could be seen.

Every child, boys and girls,
Looking up towards the skies,
Every food you could imagine,
Jacket potatoes, hot dogs and pies.

We all stood around the bonfire, nice and warm,
Please don't rain, we don't want a storm.

Now it's getting late,
The children are ready for bed,
No longer can they wait.
Goodnight, goodnight there has been such cheer,
That's it now, until next year.

Madeline Martin (14)
St Thomas More Catholic College

Writing This Poem!

Poems are difficult to write,
You try and try with all your might.
You've got some words and you make them rhyme,
But when you look up, you've lost some time.
I've got an hour to think of something good,
What rhymes with good, could, would and should?
I'm going to leave this and just let it be,
This is my poem and it's written by me.

Elisa Hearne (15)
St Thomas More Catholic College

Bonfire Night

November the 5th,
November the 5th,
Bonfire Night arrives,
Organising displays, costing a lot,
Home-made toffee apples, ready to scoff,
Guy Fawkes on top, ready to drop,
The bonfire is lit,
The fire begins to roar,
Take a step back, the heat is more,
The sky starts to glow,
The snap and crackle of the wood,
The smell of burning gets up your nose,
Your cheeks begin to glow from the fire,
I can't wait for the sparklers to appear,
Mum brings them out
With gloves in tow,
We stand arms stretched, ready to go,
The match is struck, the light begins,
I write my name over and over again,
It does not last long,
Soon they have gone,
We wait excitedly for the fireworks to begin,
The rockets are first, going to the moon,
The Catherine wheels turn so fast,
I want it to last,
The bangers are next,
The Roman candles make pretty fountains,
The volcanoes erupt with such a gust.

Alex Brough (15)
St Thomas More Catholic College

Fireworks Poem

Everyone's excited and ready for the show,
The bonfire's lit and giving out a glow,
It's packed out here,
The first one's lit, get ready for the cheer,
Fireworks.

Whoosh! Into the sky it goes, glowing bright,
We're having lots of fun tonight,
Rockets flying everywhere,
Light the next but take care,
Fireworks!

Roman candles left and right,
Shooting star, disappearing into the night,
Jumping Jacks 1, 2, 3,
Can everybody see
Fireworks?

Wow! Look at that way up in the air,
Bang, it goes just like a flare,
It's shining like a star,
Look they're landing, there they are,
Fireworks.

Smoke is oozing from the fire,
We all watch as things go higher,
The wheels go round and round,
Look what we have found,
Fireworks.

All the fireworks have gone,
The fire is burning out,
We are going to bed now,
The rain will put everything out,
Fireworks.

We woke up in the morning,
The mist is clearing well,
The fireworks and bonfire,
Still have the smoky smell,
With all the ash and cinders,
Didn't we do well!

Kim Sherwin (14)
St Thomas More Catholic College

Break Of Dawn

Guns were cocked,
Guns were fired,
Men were falling,
Men were tired,
Sound of grenades hitting the ground,
Cover your ears, it's a really loud sound.

I never knew the time would come
I'd have to fire my first-held gun.
I thought I'd missed, but I heard a sound,
Then saw a man hit the ground.
I looked around and heard a groan,
I must admit, I'm missing home.

The trenches were made,
We all jumped down,
We hid our faces from the world around,
I looked at my mate, then heard a cough,
I couldn't believe it, he'd just been shot.

We fought for weeks and the end was near,
We finally won and all gave a cheer.
I can't believe I made it home,
I don't want to hear another groan.
I went to the kitchen to get a cup of tea,
Then sat with my child, asleep on my knee.

Damian Rowe (15)
St Thomas More Catholic College

Christmas Day

Christmas is a happy time,
Everyone drinks lots of wine.
Presents under the Christmas tree
And they are nearly all for me!

The table of food laid out fine,
Christmas pud, turkey and wine.
Oh it's started to snow,
Now that has made my day.
As I look through the window
Children run out to play.

Michelle Owen (14)
St Thomas More Catholic College

In A Place

In a place where no one knows
The mountains are covered in lots of snow.

In this place no one's there,
The sun shines without a care.

In this place where no one goes,
Will anybody ever know?

Rachel Becker (15)
St Thomas More Catholic College

You

The sun shines through the curtains
And I know today will be a better day,
For I will see your face
And all of this darkness will be gone . . .
Without a trace.

Natalie Davies (15)
St Thomas More Catholic College

A Boy At War

At the start he was clean-cut and smart,
He looked the part.
All in combat, ready to fight for our country,
His country.
He was on parade with his fellow soldiers,
Finally he was ready for war.
He forced a smile and climbed on the truck.

For all the months he was away from home,
He moaned and cried.
Wanting to go home badly,
The pain was too much to handle.
He put a brave face on when fighting,
To look a strong man,
But really he was only a boy.

He was seventeen and still a child,
But still he went on fighting.
He was numb from his waist down,
The aches and pains in his little legs was unbearable.
He ate from tins in the trenches,
Wanting proper, heated grub.
Now he wanted to go home.

'Big mistake,' he shouted,
He shot the enemy.
Suddenly he felt a man in this world.
'You look one too,' said the corporal.
He would pray to God to live,
He really wanted to be able to go home,
To make his mum proud.

Only at a young age,
He never made the journey home.

Gemma Dawson (15)
St Thomas More Catholic College

Bonfire Night

The bonfire's sizzling,
The fireworks, whistling,
They shoot up high
In the crackling sky.

The fireworks sparkled bright,
As they gave people a fright.
The Guy Fawkes burns
As the fireworks return.

On the very cold night
The bonfire sparkles bright.
A firework swirls
And burns a girl!

Bang! Bang! Bang!
The fireworks sang
Up high
Into the sky.

Rachel Mannion (14)
St Thomas More Catholic College

War

The soldiers were walking from street to street,
With great big sores on their feet,
It felt like they had been walking for days,
In the mad rush one of them fell with all of the pains.

As the darkness came so did a gun fire,
The soldiers jumped up and decided to do the same,
And fired back
With their great big packs on their backs.

The commander shouted gas as all the men ran past,
Two men died so the other soldiers cried,
But they carried on with their lives,
Because the country needed them to fight.

Charlotte Preece (14)
St Thomas More Catholic College

War

The alarm clock to awaken us, sounds of shrieking missiles,
No water, no food, hiding amongst the piles.
The piles of terrified children, clinging onto their mothers,
As they wait to get food from their brothers.
Another body shot down.
As the evil get crowned.
Walking from the streets, hiding from the guns,
All we want is to have fun.
Soldiers are proud,
As they say, 'We will die for our country,' out loud.

The sun at its peak, burning-hot,
Screams getting louder like a child abandoned from its cot.
Bombs blast turning homes into rubble,
Safety schools, religious buildings all in trouble.
All hope of life swept away,
Safety for me and my family is all I pray.
Pain and suffering blasted away by streams of blood,
It is humans that have caused this flood.
Stains that have turned into mental scars couldn't be removed,
Of murders, gashes and brutal wounds.

Night arrives with the cold fear,
Will I be alive, or is my death near?
Questions whirling in and out of my head,
Wanting shelter and warmth of my bed.
Children losing hope as their bodies are left without soul,
After living a life which seemed like a fire of coal.
Family worn apart and terrified,
No hope for the future, just faces that are petrified,
Brutal murders, terrifying scars, homeless people,
Atmosphere full of pollution,
Is war the solution?

Sadia Khalil (14)
St Thomas More Catholic College

Fireworks: The Good And Bad

Flashing in the distance,
Dogs barking deep into the night,
Children's faces lifting
Whilst the fireworks are banging.

Bang after bang, light after light,
To some people this is a fright.
People are singing and dancing,
Watching the sky being lit up.

To some Bonfire Night is good,
To others it's bad for one simple reason,
Fireworks can hurt and injure
And it can wreck people's lives.

Hospitals are full of these people,
Burns over their bodies.
When they turn they are in pain,
So whatever you do, don't be stupid
And play the game safe.

Michael Howard (14)
St Thomas More Catholic College

Bonfire Night

A dark but light sky,
With fireworks sparkling bright,
A fire is burning,
With Guy Fawkes burning as he does.

The dogs were barking at the moon,
As the fireworks went by,
A lovely sight to see,
But a loud noise to hear.

As it comes to the end of them,
The noise quietens down,
They stop going off,
Oh and what a dark sight.

Russell Allen (14)
St Thomas More Catholic College

In The Trenches

I knew a small soldier boy
Who laughed at life with joy.
In the trenches so quiet and cold,
Lay him, wishing he was in his mother's hold.

Too young to know pain as some do,
Hoping not to die just yet, he knew
It would come one day,
But at least he died trying for his country.

His soul moved around,
Silent and unnoticed,
Through sleeping soldiers,
So tired and unfound.

God came down,
He followed
Up to Heaven,
Trying not to make a sound.

Stephanie Dunn (14)
St Thomas More Catholic College

I Love Football

The sound from the ball as it hits the shoe,
I can't believe we've lost to you.

Lots of stadiums all over the world,
Did you see that shot, how it curled!

Get the ball out of the net,
I've lost my money on a stupid bet.

The big rich player with a fast car,
You can kick it really far.

Win, lose or draw,
No matter the score.

I love football.

Thomas Ford (14)
St Thomas More Catholic College

Fireworks On November 5th

We are here ready and waiting,
The fireworks arrive here to entertain us.
3, 2, 1 *crash, bang, boom*, colours in the sky.
Rockets, Roman candles and Catherine wheels.
We wait in anticipation
As we wait again they fly high in the sky.
We all go to the big bonfire to get warm.
We all get ready for the big finale.
Five screamers at the same time,
The colours, blue, red, orange, green and purple,
All of us astonished by the display.
Final thoughts; awesome! Fantastic! Brilliant!
I can't wait for next year.
We all go home, sit by the fire,
Another November 5th has gone by.

Alex Thorley (14)
St Thomas More Catholic College

My Dog

My dog slobbers; don't ask me why,
He slobbers while he eats a fly.
He slobbers when he sees his tea,
He even slobbers at the sight of me!

He slobbers when he sees a tree;
A sure sign that he needs a pee!
My dog slobbers; but I love him so,
He wets my clothes; I don't scream *no!*
Instead I laugh and pat his back,
For my dog seems to have a knack,
To spend his slobber far and wide;
Yet still he's loyal at my side!

Thomas Wood (11)
St Thomas More Catholic College

The Big Blue Sea

I love the sea,
It always smiles at me,
It's like a giant blue blanket,
Crashing and bumping, but looking so calm.
It sounds like a roaring lion,
But won't do you any harm.
It tastes so salty and bitter,
No place for junk, no place for litter.
It's something you would wish,
But not to smell like fish.
It feels so cold,
But before as I told,
I love the sea,
Because it smiles at me.

Chelsea Swift (12)
St Thomas More Catholic College

Family Day

F ather at work, bored at home.
A rrogant brother, mad as ever.
M other cleaning, dust galore.
 I am me and me I am.
L azy Cheryl, listens to nothing.
Y awning to bed, what a day it's been.

D ad still up, watching films.
A h, shut up, we're going to sleep.
Y es it's over, time for bed.
S sssshhhh!

Charlotte Clayton (11)
St Thomas More Catholic College

Darkness Falls

I lie on the golden sands
And look into the sky.
The sun is blazing in my face
And blinding my eyes.

The trees are swaying,
Blowing gently in the breeze,
Then miraculously the sky turns black,
I am shaking from my shoulders to my knees.

The roaring waves are wild,
They crash against the rocks,
The leaves are violently ripped off the trees,
I stand there paralysed in shock.

It finally seems to calm down,
My heart returns back to its normal rate.
I quickly collect my belongings,
I think I will return on a later date.

Gemma Sherratt (12)
St Thomas More Catholic College

Family Poem

My sister is sly like a cat,
My dad is round but not fat.
My mum is hard-working
And that is that.

My nans are caring,
My grandads like sharing.
My pet dog Lili likes to play
And I like to do sport, all day.

Nicholas Wild (11)
St Thomas More Catholic College

Time Flies

The time is near but finally here,
With great excitement but so much fear.
I wait in desperation,
To only fill my aspiration.

So many years of education,
Another five years of devastation.
I went from being the best
To mingling in with all the rest.

But now the time has come to start afresh,
Now I'm dropping the offspring off at the crèche.
Now I can retire
And not be able to respire.

As you have guessed I am dead
And no more thoughts are running through my head.

Daniel Meigh (15)
St Thomas More Catholic College

My Bro The Bug

I can imagine my brother as a bug,
But not as a wriggly worm or a big fat slug.
And not as a creepy-crawlie woodlouse,
Or even a spider as big as our house.
Not a rock-hard beetle or a buzzy-buzz fly,
Nor a pretty shelled snail, which I think are shy.

Now my bro's not that ugly and he's not really a thug,
But he's got that smell of boys, so I think he's a . . .
Stink bug!

Sally Pepper (11)
St Thomas More Catholic College

The Haunted

As I entered the dark, long corridor
I heard a scream of a woman.
As I neared the never-ending scream
My heart started thumping wildly.
I wanted to stop and go back,
But my curiosity kept moving me forward.

I opened the door,
Creak!
I looked inside and there was nothing there,
The scream had just vanished,
But now I heard a mean, ferocious growl.
As my hand slowly reached the doorknob
I could hear the sound getting louder.

The door swung open,
I looked around and there was nothing there.
All of a sudden I felt a sharp pain
Going through my body,
In a few seconds everything went black.

Usman Fayaz (13)
St Thomas More Catholic College

My Dog

My dog is the best of the rest,
He's very nice when we're around,
Day in, day out he's always barking
And that's when we start to shout.

My dog is the nicest you've ever seen,
He's always looking for me,
His name is Bruce or Brucey Baby,
He acts like someone who's never been fed.
But this is my dog and this is me,
I love my dog and that is the way it's got to stay.

James Allen (11)
St Thomas More Catholic College

Healthy Eating

Pizza and chips,
Lemon and lime,
Hurry and brush your teeth
Before you run out of time.

Tea and biscuits,
Chocolates and crisps,
Aren't very nice,
Never try them twice.

Cakes and sweets,
Aren't better than meats,
Don't give in,
Put 'em in the bin.

Don't eat the junk,
Or you'll end up a lump,
Only eat healthy,
If you want to be wealthy.

Say hello to good food,
If you wanna be in a good mood,
Don't eat bad
Or you'll end up sad.

Abu-Bakr Binyameen (12)
St Thomas More Catholic College

Brothers

Brothers can be	B	ig
Brothers are sometimes	R	otten
Evil	O	nes
Some are	T	iny
Some are	H	eroes
Some love	E	veryone
But they're still little	R	otters
Some make you	S	cream!

Christopher Simpson (11)
St Thomas More Catholic College

A Sad Tale Of World War I

Grime and wet,
Dirt and wretched smells,
Life in the trenches, it's no paradise.
Soldiers hurt, blood and the dead,
We're not that far off.

He signed up thinking it wouldn't be bad,
'It'll last a week,' he said,
'It will all be over before you can say . . .'
Bang,
Shot dead in the trenches.
So much life, so much life,
But it all ended with one bullet,
That's all it took.

Four years later the war ended.
How they rejoiced after the ending of a horrific battle.
'It's over, it's over,' they cried.
But what's there to rejoice?
Families have lost their sons or daughters,
There's nothing to rejoice about that,
We have lost millions during the war,
The war,
The war to end all wars.

Liam Blackshaw (14)
St Thomas More Catholic College

The Sea

T he sea is like a crumpled, blue blanket,
H orses galloping is what it is,
E merald sea, blue and shiny in the sun.

S lap of coldness is what it feels like,
E very summer it smells and tastes of salt,
A rray of blue ripples.

Stephanie Lomas (12)
St Thomas More Catholic College

My Family

My family is really fantastic,
I couldn't ask for a better one.
If someone is upset or feeling down
They always get cheered up.
All you have to do is look at them
And a grin appears on your face.
It's like a clown at a circus,
Trying hard not to smile!
My brother is like a leaping tiger,
Always full of energy.
My sister is like a monkey,
Always hanging out with her friends.
My dad is like a big grizzly bear,
Something to snuggle up to!
My mum is like a taxi,
Always running people around!
And I just like to be with my family,
Or hang out with my cool friends.

Lauren Brereton (11)
St Thomas More Catholic College

Seaside

S alty water makes my tongue tizzle,
E meralds shine in the sea,
A sea is like a roaring lion,
S ea is like a crumpled, warm, dark blue blanket,
I like to watch as fish swim by from a tall boat way up high,
D etermined to swim and splash in the sea with a beach ball,
E verywhere I go is to see the waves crash on the rocks.

Ruth Whitehouse (12)
St Thomas More Catholic College

Angel Or Devil?

My sister,
Runs off with my things,
But always returns them.
Puts on DVDs when I have asked,
But then she watches them upstairs.
Angel or Devil?

My sister,
Shouts at me,
But says sorry.
Jumps on me when I'm asleep,
But then goes away.
Angel or Devil?

My sister,
Interrupts when I'm doing homework,
But usually for a good reason.
Gets me into trouble,
But I love her.
So what do you think?
Angel or Devil?

Laura Corbishley (13)
St Thomas More Catholic College

Seaside

S alty waters cover me,
E verywhere is surrounded by
A n array of blue ripples, I can see
S andy beaches washed away,
I nside that sea there is something out there I should see.
D own in the ocean deeper than can be,
E verywhere there is fish.

Laura Shea (13)
St Thomas More Catholic College

My Brother

Look out,
My bro's about,
Cute he may be
And runs about with glee,
But he messes up my room
And leaves me in gloom.
I get the blame,
He's so hard to tame,
But then a picture he draws me
And starts to plea,
He wants me to be his mate,
When he does this I find him great,
I give in,
He gives me a grin,
He's really not that bad,
To have him, really, I'm quite glad!

Rachel Worthington (12)
St Thomas More Catholic College

Fireworks

Red, green, purple and blue,
I watched the fireworks as they flew.
Banging, flashing and squeals
As we watched the Catherine wheels.

The night was dark
And the dogs would bark
As we watched the fireworks
From the park.

As the sky lit up and the people glared
The flames from the fire flared.

As the night came to an end,
From the corner of my eye
I saw a rocket fly into the sky.

Stephanie Hubbert (14)
St Thomas More Catholic College

The World-Wide Sea

The sea is like a blue, crumpled blanket,
It is like a cold hankie,
It sounds like a loud splash in the bath,
You can never open your mouth to laugh,
It tastes like strong salt,
It's dead hard to swim out for it's like trying to win the vault,
it feels like a cold slap,
Instead of getting your hair wet you are relying on your cap,
It smells like a fish,
I hoped it was like a Jacuzzi but that was only a wish.

Grant Saville (12)
St Thomas More Catholic College

The Seaside

S alty and bitter,
E ternally blue,
A n array of blue ripples,
S lapping against the rocks,
 I mitating the sound of a vicious, hungry lion,
D isguised as a deadly killing machine,
E verlasting emerald sea.

Elliot W H Birks (12)
St Thomas More Catholic College

At The Seaside

S mashing waves against the rocks,
E normous sea covers the Earth,
A wful taste of salt, it's bitter,
S *hh* upon the shore,
 I t feels like a warm bath,
D eep as it could be,
E xtraordinary creature in the sea.

Rochelle Tonks (12)
St Thomas More Catholic College

The Sea

The sea is nice and blue,
If you look at it properly it is beautiful too.
The sea is peaceful and quiet,
It sometimes causes a riot.
The fish in the sea
They swim with happiness and glee.
The sea makes a big splash,
Sometimes the sea makes a crash.

Ataf Hussain (13)
St Thomas More Catholic College

Seaside

The . . .

S izzling sea slides so smoothly,
E merald sea, roars like a lion,
A cross the bitter ocean, it's running for help.
S plashing like a helpless fish,
I nside the crashing sea was a fish to let free.
D ashing, came the sea upon the shore,
E choed, came a dolphin as it sorrily cried.

Rebekah Burt (12)
St Thomas More Catholic College

The Seaside

S ome seas are a salty group of galloping horses,
E verybody loves to lie in that large, crumpled, blue blanket.
A bittersweet taste from a large roaring lion,
S weet sensation from my special, warm bath.
I t is sometimes a huge pair of large, blue jaws.
D ay and night the waves clap and clash.
E very time I sit by the sea it feels like it is singing with me.

Joshua Heaton (13)
St Thomas More Catholic College

Man U And Chelsea

Man U, Man U, always scoring goals,
Man U, Man U, quickly put on Scholes.
As the minutes go by,
Man U keep on scoring high.
So watch out Chelsea, 'cause without no doubt
We will kick you out.
So Man U fans shout,
Shout, shout!

Man U, Man U, always scoring goals,
Man U, Man U, fighting with their souls.

Man U, Man U, wearing red,
While I'm eating my loaf of bread
And here comes my best friend Ted,
While I'm watching TV in the shed.

Man U, Man U, we're going rubbish,
It was getting boring, I had a stitch,
Then I supported Chelsea
And I had a friend named Lee.
Then I thought of a song,
It was so hard, I kept on scratching my tongue,
It goes like this, that you wouldn't miss.

Chelsea, Chelsea, they love me,
Chelsea, Chelsea, have a cup of tea
And then it goes on and off,
It's just I told Man U to buzz off.

Jonathon James (13)
St Thomas More Catholic College

The Ghost Ship

Upon this ghostly ship I fear,
A strange poltergeist is very near.
The slightest creak,
Sends my nerves feeling really weak.

As I lay here waiting for morning,
Torrential rain is fiercely pouring.
Each day I long to witness the sun,
For then I know the deed is done.

This ship is famously haunted by a ghost,
Who rules the waves and rules the coast.
A male ghoul rarely shows,
Nothing passes from under his nose.

He watches over deep sea creatures,
A long, black cape hides his unsightly features.
His pale white skin,
No next of kin.

Be afraid when you hear his cries,
Beware; do not dare meet his cold, grey eyes.

Hannah Wegierak (12)
St Thomas More Catholic College

Shark Attack

The shock of the cold water
Elbows and knees in shock
Angelfish floating through the water
Sharks attack
Excitement in a frenzy of waves.

Nathan Atkinson (12)
St Thomas More Catholic College

Winter

A pure white blanket surrounds the land,
making it very bare, bleak and bland.
The cold winter sun hides in the cloudy sky,
hardly noticeable, as if it is shy.

The frost is like demons biting at your skin,
with tiny little teeth, sharper than a pin.
Sparkling icicles hanging from ledges,
opal-white snow clinging on hedges.

The frozen lake glistens, shinier than gold,
and snowflakes fall, extremely cold.

However, this majestic beauty will soon be gone,
for the winter sun has crept out and shone,
leaving dirty grey snow and sleet,
the magnificent carpet of snow, melted from the heat.

Joy Hawley (12)
St Thomas More Catholic College

The Bully

Her heart throbbing, her teeth clenched
Her eyes streaming, her body drenched
with fear.

Her knees shaking, her eyes closed
Her eyes burning, she supposed
they weren't near.

Her lips trembling, her body weakened
Her shoulders relaxing, the door creaked . . .
Bang!

Atikah Ayaz (12)
St Thomas More Catholic College

The Butterflies

Butterflies come in all shapes and sizes
And different colours too
Symmetrical, small and big
Red, orange, green or blue.

They have good camouflage
When you've caught one, it'll get away
It's small and fast and speedy
Don't expect it to stay.

They come in warm seasons
Especially in the sky
Swooping far down below
Then continuing up high.

Everyone likes butterflies
Including me and you
They wind around rainbows
Like angels too.

Jennifer Huson (12)
St Thomas More Catholic College

The Blue Sea

Whenever I go to the seaside
I see three galloping horses racing for freedom
As the wind begins to stop the mighty blow with power
You can hear the whisper of terrified shells as they cry for help
And rattles among each other
As the water drowns them from daylight.

They are glad and cheerful
As they see the sunlight glisten and glow with wonder
To thank us for rescuing them.
As I step into the bitter water
Suddenly a mighty slap warning me to stay away.
The roar with power as it attacks the innocent rocks
You can hear the whisper of the trickling river.

Adena Lawrence (12)
St Thomas More Catholic College

Life Is . . .

Life is a flower that blossoms in the spring,
Life is the birds that chirp outside and sing.
Life is like a maze with many closed ends,
But life is a gift to be treasured with close friends.

Life is like a book, you don't know what's in store,
Life is given to everyone, both the rich and the poor.
Life is the beginning of a beautiful start;
So don't be foolish and look after your heart.

Carrieann Machin (12)
St Thomas More Catholic College

Seaside

S eaweed waving under the water
E ating ice cream on the hot beach
A woken by the crashing waves smashing on the beach
S plashing up the rocks
I ce melting like an ice cream
D iamonds sparkly like the waves on the shore
E meralds across the sea sparkling.

Katy Louise Watkiss (12)
St Thomas More Catholic College

My Poem

The sea is like a blue blanket
Dark black sky and fluffy clouds
It sounds like crashing in the deep
It tastes like soggy fish fingers
It feels so cold and freezing.

Kurt Newton (12)
St Thomas More Catholic College

The Sea

The sea looks like an emerald shining really brightly
With pearls and blue ripples
Swaying very lightly

The sea sounds like a lion
Roaring and fiercely crashing
The sea can be calm
Rolling gently and splashing

The sea tastes very salty
Very bitter too
You try to get it out of your mouth
But there's nothing you can do

The sea feels like a cold slap
When the waves hit your legs
Or it can feel like a warm bath
Warm on both your legs

The sea smells like fishes most
Probably because they're in there
The sea also smells salty
Because there's salt everywhere.

Katie Ford (12)
St Thomas More Catholic College

The Sea

T onnes of cold water spreading on your body
H orses galloping delightfully and loudly
E merald sea, so smooth, silky and very glittery

S ea tastes of seaweed and salt
E very day is an endless space of excitement and possibility
A sound so powerful like a roaring lion.

Rosie Hogan (12)
St Thomas More Catholic College

Autumn

The leaves are falling,
The nights are drawing in,
Summer has ended,
Autumn will begin.

The leaves are changing colour,
And fall off the trees,
As days are getting colder,
And the ground begins to freeze.

Soon it will be Hallowe'en,
When children knock on your door,
With scary masks for trick or treat,
And chocolate sweets and more.

Bonfire night will soon be here,
With fires on every hill,
Bangs, sparkles and flashing lights,
Which gives us all a thrill.

Autumn is ending,
Winter's on its way,
Time for snowmen, presents,
And Santa who's on his sleigh.

Tom Daniel (12)
St Thomas More Catholic College

My Grandad

G randad is great, gentle and kind
R eally sleepy, tired all the time
A nnoying sometimes when he calls me 'Bluebell'
N ever makes me feel like I'm in Hell
D ances like a fool
A nd sings like a cat
D isastrous hair, he needs a hat!

Lois Stevenson (11)
St Thomas More Catholic College

My Emotion

I feel it in the morning,
I feel it in the night,
I feel it when I'm yawning,
I feel it when I fight.

I feel it when I scream,
I feel it when I shout,
I feel it when I'm walking
Out and about.

I feel it when I'm talking,
I feel it when I sigh,
I feel it when I'm walking,
I feel the end is nigh.

The thing I feel is weak,
The thing I feel is strong,
The thing I feel is right,
The thing I feel is wrong.

The thing I feel has no cure,
And it has no potion,
For the thing I feel
Is a very powerful emotion.

Michael Plant (12)
St Thomas More Catholic College

Family

F orever cleaning is my mum
A lways shouting is my dad
M ostly fighting for me and my brothers
I and my brothers forever eating
L eft out never
Y ou will never find anything better.

Joel Niemczyk (11)
St Thomas More Catholic College

My Sister

I've got a sister
She annoys me like a blister
She's a weapon of mass destraction
But she acts like she owns a mansion.

She's a moody old bag
She's a never-ending nag
She's a fierce steaming bull
To me she's awful.

She's a sly fiendish foe
She's evil from head to toe
If she can't get her way
There's no keeping her at bay

She thinks she's bling bling
Always wearing a ring
She's a right drama queen
At the age of sixteen.

Jake Rushton (12)
St Thomas More Catholic College

Brother Poem

He is running along the corridor,
He is running after me,
He bursts through my bedroom door then he shouts at me,
'Give me that remote! Give it to me now!'
If you ever want to see the daylight I suggest you give it me now.
My brother is always transfixed onto the telly,
At this minute he is probably watching the video to the rap star Nelly.

Rebecca Howells (11)
St Thomas More Catholic College

My Love

To my love,
Just like a dove,
I would not dare,
To be aware,
This love is magnificent,
And sweet smelling too,
You are the sun,
And you are the one.

You are the person,
Who changes the season,
The one who cares,
Who always shares,
You are the one,
Who broke my heart,
The girl I love,
And who I will never forget.

My final word,
For the bird,
I now must forget,
The girl I met,
That this love has ended,
Now that you have told me,
You will not be important,
To me.

Geoffrey Knott (12)
St Thomas More Catholic College

My Family

F riendly
A nnoying
M erciful
I ntelligent
L oving
Y outhful.

Danielle Jenkinson (11)
St Thomas More Catholic College

The Big Match

Every Saturday afternoon,
People support their local team,
And when one of the players score,
Some of the fans will shout and scream.

Enter the teams like gladiators,
The crowd start shouting for blood,
The referee comes out in black,
'Oh not him, he's no good!

David Beckham to Roy Keane,
Roy Keane to Paul Scholes.
Scholes shoots and he scores,
Now he has two goals.

1-0. 2-0, 3-0,
The score keeps going up.
Fans cheer at the end of the match,
Their team has won the cup.

The winners they are strong
The losers they look bleak,
Oh well, it doesn't matter,
They'll just have to win next week.

Thomas Lavelle (12)
St Thomas More Catholic College

My Family Poem

My dog sleeps like a log,
He snores like a hog.
He is a brill lad,
But is a bit mad.
My mum is a fab mum,
She always gives a hum.
My sister is like a blister,
I never say I've missed her,
I love them all like my football.

Jack Gratton (11)
St Thomas More Catholic College

The Noises Of Hallowe'en

I hear a ghost
It's coming close

I hear a witch
Her voice high-pitched

I hear footsteps far away
They are coming closer the more I pray

I'm scared now, shaking to the bone
I don't want to be here, I want to be home

I get on my knees and pray by my bed
And start to think, *I wish I was dead*

My wish came true and that was the end of me
I'm dead in Heaven but I'll haunt on Hallowe'en.

Amy Cross (12)
St Thomas More Catholic College

My Hamster

My hamster is very loud,
and he's white and brown.

In the day,
and at night he plays,
just to keep me awake.

My hamster loves his food,
but how he eats it is very crude.

My hamster always nibbles,
and it's very horrible,
because his teeth are yellow.

Kieran Smith (11)
St Thomas More Catholic College

Nature At Its Finest

As you stare outside,
Watching the trees glide,
The distant chatter of people,
As you look out you can see the church steeple.

The land coated by mist and fog
You can hear the faint cry of a dog
The birds tweeting
As you hear the sheep bleating.

Smelling the freshly cut lawn
As it just becomes dawn
As the kite's flying high
Feel the coldness as it whisks by
As I glance for a final time
As I hear the church bells chime.

Sophie Cork (12)
St Thomas More Catholic College

Eyes

When I see the sunrise
I think of the glow within your eyes
Eyes that sparkle, oh so bright
Like the stars in the night
Eyes so dark, clear and deep
I can see them even in my sleep
Eyes that show so much trust
I have to take it, that I must
Your love for me is far and wide
I feel a shiver deep inside
When you sleep just like a log
That's my Snowy, that's my dog.

Lucy Whitfield (12)
St Thomas More Catholic College

Trick Or Treat

The sky is dark
And witches lurk
In the shadows
Ghouls smirk.

A knock on my door
I can hear it now
Saying, 'Answer the door'
Causing a row.

Cautiously I get
Up from my chair
Shouting all the while
Asking, 'Who's there?'

I open the door
And, oh what a fright
3 witches, 2 ghouls
Haunt through the night.

One asks me for money
The one with horrid feet
The other wants candy
Trick or treat.

Sarah Griffiths (13)
St Thomas More Catholic College

My Family

F ather is as lazy as a cat, he sometimes acts like my pet rat
A nd my sister Jade likes to drink a lot of lemonade
M y mum likes to do all the housework and is sick of my dad
buying Mercs
I like to play on my PlayStation
L anky Lucy is my pet cat who likes to lie on the kitchen mat
Y apping Shona the house moaner is a bit of a groaner.

Rhiannon Colclough (11)
St Thomas More Catholic College

My Strange Cake

In my mixture I will put
a dozen of warm hazelnuts.

A box of eggs
mixed together with juicy frogs' legs.

Stir in a little BBQ sauce
it will make a lovely third course.

Put it in the oven at gas mark four,
make sure you close the oven door.

Leave it in for an hour,
so it will become extra sour.

Take it out and let it cool,
keep it away from any fool.

Invite your friends over for tea,
and let them taste your speciality.

Liam Brannigan (12)
St Thomas More Catholic College

My Family Poem

My mum is very funny,
She makes me laugh a lot,
But when I'm being cheeky,
She just loses the plot.

My dad is sometimes bossy,
He gets quite stressed and that,
But when I'm being naughty,
I get my lucky hat.

My sister, she's quite moody,
She moans and groans all day,
She thinks I'm so annoying,
So I jump and shout, 'Hey!'

Rachel Dimmock (11)
St Thomas More Catholic College

Love

He holds me,
Cuddles me,
Makes me safe.
I can smell his soft hands around my body,
Holding me,
Comforting me.
His heart beats in my ear,
I can feel it,
I can fondle it.
I can feel my heart staring at his,
The bridge is building,
I love him,
You can see it in my eyes.
I'm stuck in my bubble with him,
And our love.

Carmen Gater (13)
Sir Thomas Boughey High School

Why Do We?

Why do we fight on land to be,
and in the air and across the sea?
Why do we fight on fields of green?
That because of us have become obscene.
Why do we fight with other lands?
Why do they give guns to children's hands?
Why do we sit here and watch people burn,
when we could join together and really learn
what this fighting is all about?
Now come on and help me kick terrorism out.

Stephen Birch (14)
Sir Thomas Boughey High School

Lost Memories

Of all the memories I've had,
Not one comes to mind,
I find it hard to choose,
All linked together by rope binds,
I can't unlock the good ones,
Or lock up the bad,
Sometimes I feel locked up inside,
And mad!

I can't unlock the excitement, danger or freedom,
I can't even unlock the memories which were most fun,
I wish I could free them,
I wish I could be them,
Remake them,
Unlock all those things I've achieved,
Unlock all of those memories.

Nicola Platt (13)
Sir Thomas Boughey High School

The Long Road's End

What fires burn within my heart and force me to contend
with the perils that await me at this tragic journey's end?
I have walked the roads that led to Hell;
I have challenged all but fate,
I have thought and bled
and carried on just to reach this final gate.
And now the task before me looms
This dire deed undone.
What fear or wound could ever still this last defiant cry?
I shall make my stand against the shadow
'neath the endless burning sky.

Jake Peever (14)
Sir Thomas Boughey High School

A Piece Of Hope

Sometimes I want to walk over broken glass
Just to feel it between my toes
Most of the time you're rewarded for being rational
Every so often you want to stay in bed all day
And laugh into the covers.

Sometimes I want to disappear
Just for the new experience
Most of the time you need to feel just a tiny bit loved
Every so often you want to sleep
Until your eyes never open.

Sometimes I'm blinded by troubles that face me
Just like fearing death instead of enjoying life
Most of the time I ignore the presence of good
Every so often I want to scream and cry the problems away.

And until I strive through it
The reward is not earned, nor mine.

Samantha Brooks (13)
Sir Thomas Boughey High School